The Manchester Museum:

Window *to the World*

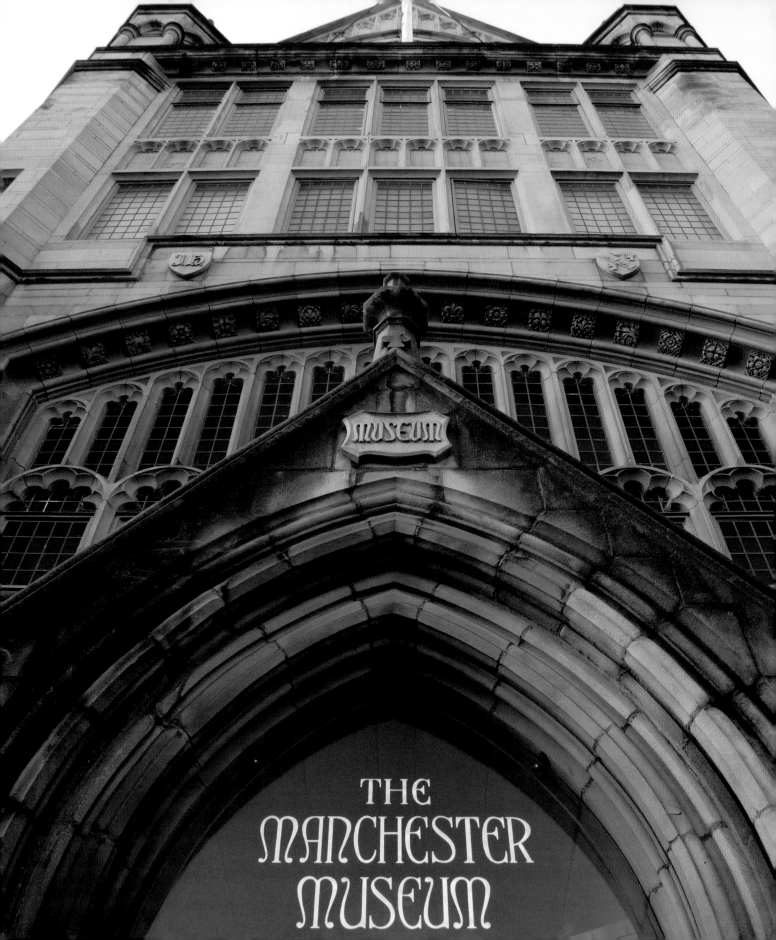

The Manchester Museum:

Window to the World

The Manchester Museum: Window to the World

© 2012 The Manchester Museum

First published in 2012 by The Manchester Museum

ISBN 978 1 906507 81 7

Designed and produced by
Third Millennium Information / www.tmiltd.com

Edited by Dmitri Logunov and Nick Merriman
Design by Matthew Wilson
Production by Bonnie Murray
Reprographics by Studio Fasoli, Italy
Printed by Printer Trento, Italy

The University of Manchester
The Manchester Museum

Supported using public funding by
ARTS COUNCIL ENGLAND

Contents

Foreword   6

Contributors and Acknowledgements   8

Introduction   10

Section 1: Hidden treasures

01 Tales from ancient worlds   22

02 Living and dying under the pharaohs   34

03 Collecting cultures, making connections   46

04 History and geography in the palm of your hand 58

05 The story of Earth and early life   66

06 A is for Aardvark, Z is for Zebra   76

07 A collection of inordinate number and diversity 84

08 All the green things upon the earth   94

09 Live animals, conservation through education 104

10 Investigating and preserving the collections 112

Section 2: Using the collections

11 Collection-based research   122

12 Making sense of our world: learning from collections 132

13 Close encounters: engagement and participation in the 138
    Museum and beyond

14 Search us online   146

Further reading   150

Picture credits   156

Foreword

The Manchester Museum has been part of the University of Manchester for nearly 150 years. Over this time it has grown to become the largest university museum in the UK. Alongside the Whitworth Art Gallery, John Rylands Library (Deansgate) and Jodrell Bank Discovery Centre, it is one of the University's major cultural assets, providing inspiration and enjoyment to a wide audience, from local people to international visitors.

A university museum like the Manchester Museum has a variety of functions. It originally became part of the University so that its collections could be used both for teaching and for research in the new academic disciplines that were taking shape in the late 19th century. This remains a vital role, and each year the Museum contributes to dozens of courses across the University. It also supports hundreds of research activities.

More recently, universities have also begun to play an increasingly significant role in the wider society around them. We are passionately committed to this at the University of Manchester, and the Manchester Museum is one of our most important means of engaging with our local community. Each year it hosts visits from thousands of pupils from local schools and colleges and works intensively with community groups. We are proud to have such a dynamic and accessible museum as part of the University.

Professor Dame Nancy Rothwell
President and Vice-Chancellor
The University of Manchester

Above: Fired clay lamp of the 'cocked hat' type found at Carthage in North Africa and dating from the 6th–5th centuries BC. The twin nozzles each held a wick of twisted fibre. The flame at the end of the wick burned as long as there was olive or fish oil in the lamp.

Contributors and Acknowledgements

BOOK CONTRIBUTORS

Introduction: Nick Merriman (Director); *Chapter 1*: Bryan Sitch (Deputy Head of Collections and Curator of Archaeology); *Chapter 2*: Campbell Price (Curator of Egypt and Sudan); *Chapter 3*: Stephen Welsh (Curator of Living Cultures); *Chapter 4*: Keith Sugden (Curator of Numismatics); *Chapter 5*: David Gelsthorpe (Curator of Earth Science Collections); *Chapter 6*: Henry McGhie (Head of Collections and Curator of Zoology); *Chapter 7*: Dmitri Logunov (Curator of Arthropods); *Chapter 8*: Rachel Webster (Curator of Botany); *Chapter 9*: Andrew Gray (Curator of Herpetology); *Chapter 10*: Samantha Sportun (Senior Conservator); *Chapter 11*: Dmitri Logunov, David Gelsthorpe, Andrew Gray, John Prag (Professor Emeritus of Archaeological Studies and of Classics), Campbell Price and Phyllis Stoddart (Resource Centre Administrator); *Chapter 12*: Esme Ward (Head of Learning and Engagement) and Anna Bunney (Curator of Public Programmes); *Chapter 13*: Esme Ward and Dmitri Logunov;

Chapter 14: Stephen Devine (New Media Officer) and Alexa Jeanes (Lead Educator).

PHOTOGRAPHY

Unless otherwise specified (see p. 156), the images were made by Paul Cliff and Victoria Haydn (Manchester, UK).

ACKNOWLEDGEMENTS

The production of this book would have been impossible without the generous support of colleagues at the Manchester Museum, who have provided us with various information and assistance: Lindy Crewe (Research Fellow in Archaeology), Jenny Discombe (Conservator), Roy Garner (former Conservator), Kate Glynn (Volunteer Co-ordinator), Velson Horie (former Conservator), Corinne Leader (Marketing Officer), Lindsey Loughtman (Curatorial Assistant, Botany), Cat Lumb (Secondary and Post-16 Coordinator), Tim Manley (Head of Marketing and Communications), Susan Martin (Curatorial Assistant, Human Cultures), Menaka Munro (Curator of Learning,

Above: Australian Trumpet *(Syrinx aruanus)*, the largest living snail species in the world.

University of Manchester; Dr David Penney of the Faculty of Life Sciences (University of Manchester) for useful suggestions and assistance during the preparation of this book; Dr Paul Bahn, archaeologist and author, for permission to quote from the *Bluffer's Guide to Archaeology*; Ros Westwood, Derbyshire Museums Manager, Buxton Museum and Art Gallery, and Jill Cook, Curator of Palaeolithic and Mesolithic collections and Deputy Keeper of the Department of Prehistory and Early Europe at the British Museum, for the dates of the 19th-century excavators of Creswell Crags; Dr Paul Holder of the John Rylands Library (University of Manchester), who translated the inscription on the Roman altar found in Manchester in 2008 and published the Roman auxiliary diploma from Ravenglass; Dr Robert Stoddart of the University of Manchester and Dr Robert Connolly, lecturer in Physical Anthropology in the Department of Anatomy at the University of Liverpool, who kindly examined the Heronbridge skeletons; Ian Mason, Archives Manager East Riding of Yorkshire Archives Service regarding the photograph of Boyd Dawkins and the Morfitt family; Oswaldo Chinchilla, Museo Popol Vuh, Universidad Francisco Marroquin (Guatemala); Richard Sivill, local historian and archivist (Atherton Parish, UK); Paul Pettitt, Senior Lecturer in Palaeolithic Archaeology, University of Sheffield; and the staff at Chetham's Library, Manchester.

Primary), Irit Narkiss (Conservator), Phillip Rispin (Curatorial Assistant, Entomology), Abigail Stevens (Environmental Conservator), Andrea Winn (Curator of Community Exhibitions) and Michael Whitworth (Head of Commercial Operations).

For valuable assistance and help in background research we also wish to thank Lucy Creighton, postgraduate student in Art Gallery and Museum Studies, University of Manchester (UK); John Piprani, postgraduate student in Archaeology,

Special thanks are also due to the contributors who have devoted their time to writing up the 'Expert Spotlight' columns: Kostas Arvanitis (*chapter 12*), Amanda Bamford (*chapter 9*), Roland Ennos (*chapter 6*), Melanie Giles (*chapter 1*), Velson Horie (*chapter 10*), Minsung Kim (*chapter 8*), Phillip Manning (*chapter 5*), Sandy O'Sullivan (*chapter 3*), Richard Preziosi (*chapter 7*) and Joyce Tyldesley (*chapter 2*).

hands on

*Every Professor of a branch of science
requires a museum and a laboratory for his
department; and accordingly in all our great
universities we have museums … each subject
taught having its own appropriate collection.*

David Murray (1904)

Introduction

Opposite: Handling tables allow the public to touch Museum specimens and are an effective way of engaging with visitors.

Below: The Manchester Museum's predecessor in Manchester town centre on Peter Street, next to the theatre, 1830.

The Manchester Museum is one of the leading examples of a type of museum that sprang from the emerging popular interest in understanding the ancient and contemporary worlds from the beginning of the 19th century, and which reached their peak during the period of the British Empire (approximately in the century 1850–1950). These 'encyclopaedic' museums, as they are often called, were physical manifestations of the optimistic ethos that fuelled Victorian and Edwardian science, that ultimately the entire world was knowable through rational enquiry.

We should remember that issues such as the age of the Earth, the development of life, and the origin and nature of the world's different cultures and people, which are today taken for granted or well understood, were in the 19th century issues of major intellectual and religious importance, as new discoveries began to challenge the assumptions by which people had lived their lives for millennia.

Initially it was groups of individuals who amassed collections of natural and 'artificial' material as part of their passion for the development of a specific subject. In Manchester these included people such as Charles Bailey and James Cosmo Melvill (botany), Robert Lloyd (entomology and Japanese ethnology), and Jesse Haworth (egyptology), whose contributions will be outlined in later sections. Their wealth generally came from their positions as manufacturers and traders in what was the world's first industrial city. The growth of industries such as textiles, particularly cotton, led to a transformation both of the appearance of the city and of the fortunes of the industrial leaders. Their newly acquired riches

11

enabled them to pursue interests suitable for men of their standing, including collecting interesting material from all around the world through their international trade contacts and through dealers and auctioneers.

There was already a tradition for such individuals to band together in formal societies where they could share knowledge and debate the issues of the day, with the Manchester Literary and Philosophical Society (founded 1781) being the most celebrated example. The Manchester Society for the Promotion of Natural History was formed in 1821 by a group of collectors and gentleman-scholars, principally to purchase and house the collections of John Leigh Phillips (1761–1814) and Thomas Henry Robinson. By 1835 the Society was sufficiently well-established to open its own purpose-built museum in the centre of Manchester, on Peter Street, near the site of the famous Peterloo Massacre of 1819. The site of the Museum is now marked by 'Museum Street' at the junction with Peter Street.

This original museum focused on natural history, with the collections of the Manchester Geological Society joining it by 1853. Typically for the time, it included, alongside the scientifically arranged specimens, groups of material that had more of the flavour of the curio or the fair. These included the mummy of Hannah Beswick, a woman who was allegedly so fearful of grave robbing that she had had her body embalmed; the unwrapped mummy of Asru, a temple singer from Ancient Egypt (see p. 35); and 'Mr Potter's Cow', a stuffed specimen of a rare breed of 'wild' white cattle.

By the 1860s, however, the Society and its museum – which visitors had to pay a small fee to see – were struggling to cope with the competition from new free municipal museums, such as Peel Park in Salford, founded following the Public Libraries and

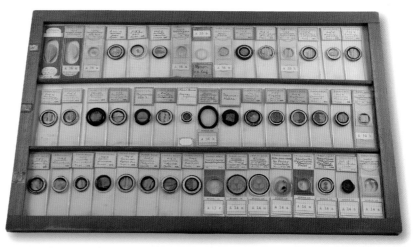

Above: Microscope slides from Charles Bailey, whose extensive botanical collection was donated to the Museum in 1917, increasing the size and importance of the Manchester Herbarium.

Left: 'Mr Potter's Cow', a mounted specimen of the British White breed of cattle. The cow, which died in 1837, is among the oldest mounted specimens in the Museum.

Museums Act of 1845, with declining membership and waning interest. After fruitless discussions with Manchester Corporation about its future, Owens College agreed to take it over in 1868, funded by the sale of the Peter Street site, so that the collections

Above: A watercolour showing Alfred Waterhouse's scheme for the Manchester Museum as part of Owen's College (later the University of Manchester), c. 1880.

Below: One of the old museum's registers, which for decades have been used to record new acquisitions to the Manchester Museum.

could be used for teaching their students in new and emerging disciplines such as geology, palaeontology and zoology, and so that they could be researched by the lecturers. Significantly, the College had plans to move to a new more spacious campus on Oxford Road in Chorlton-on-Medlock, designed by the young Alfred Waterhouse. Accordingly, plans were made to establish a new museum to house the collections on the new site, advised by Thomas Henry Huxley (1825–95), the prominent proponent of ideas of evolution nicknamed 'Darwin's bulldog'.

Waterhouse designed a monumental Gothic building which formed the western side of the campus and finally opened to the public in 1890. It comprised four floors of galleries and a herbarium on the top floor open by appointment. These galleries, including the magnificent three-storey atrium typical of museums of the period, can still be seen today with most of their original cases, redisplayed to modern standards. This type of museum represented a new kind of public space, which women as well as men could visit, and – at least in theory – all classes of people were admitted. Alongside the parks and public libraries, they were places which were alternatives to the public house, and where people could stroll, and gaze both at each other and at the displays.

The original layout of the Museum was fundamentally shaped by the Museum's first curator, William Boyd Dawkins (1837–1929). As will be seen in later sections (pp. 23–5, 67), Dawkins was one of the leading museum curators of his era, conducting his own groundbreaking fieldwork on early human occupation of Britain, and his arrangement of the galleries still has a fundamental effect on what visitors see today. The ground floor consisted of mineralogy and the earliest history of the Earth, proceeding through the fossils of the simplest organisms to the end of the Ice Age. Displays on subsequent floors included a vaguely evolutionary sequence of animals, and rooms with botany displays in side rooms.

From its outset the Museum was predominantly a natural history museum, whose collections were regularly added to by staff and other collectors. However, Dawkins' original evolutionary sequence included early human stone tools, later archaeology from Ancient Egypt and the Mediterranean, and ethnographic items from contemporary non-Western cultures. Although a few additions to these cultural collections were

Left: The first Egyptology gallery constructed in the Museum's extension funded by Jesse Haworth, c.1913.

easily accommodated, this was a different matter when it came to the large collection of Egyptology amassed by the textile magnate Jesse Haworth (see also p. 36).

In 1905, Haworth offered to donate his entire collection to the Museum, and later offered the huge sum of £5,000 towards the construction of a new building to house it. A public appeal was set up which raised a further £3,000, and construction began to designs by Alfred Waterhouse's son Paul. This building, in 'hotel de ville' style, opened in 1912, linked to the original building by a first-floor bridge. Such was the interest in providing expanded space for the human cultures collections that Haworth provided a further sum before it was even completed, for an extension which opened in 1913. Whilst the ground floors of these two extensions continued the

> **"***Fantastic exhibits, friendly staff, excellent facilities.***"**
>
> Museum visitor

sequence of the original museum by being devoted to minerology, petrology and economic geology, the upper floors consisted of Egyptology, with small amounts of ethnography, prehistory, numismatics, and Mediterranean archaeology. This division of the Museum into an original building principally focused on natural history, and a further series devoted to human cultures essentially persists today.

Jesse Haworth's fundamental influence continued after his death in 1921 when he left £30,000 in his will for a further extension to the Museum to accommodate the ever-increasing cultural collections. Accordingly in 1927 a further extension, designed now by Alfred Waterhouse's grandson Michael, opened housing displays of ethnology in what was described as a 'geographical and racial scheme', with coins and medals on the next floor, and Western European and Mediterranean archaeology

on the third floor. This represented the last major physical change to the Museum for 50 years.

Between the two world wars, collecting in the Museum continued apace, filling gaps in the 'encyclopaedic' scheme to which the various museum disciplines subscribed. At the same time, visitors began to increase from a baseline of around 50,000 in 1900, to around 150,000 a year after the 1927 extension opened. This included thousands of schoolchildren, whose teachers brought them to the Museum and other attractions when schools were requisitioned for military purposes during the First World War, and who continued the practice afterwards.

After the Second World War, collecting began to decline as Britain's colonies became independent, whilst an increased focus emerged on providing more facilities for the public. David Owen, who

Below: Facade of the Museum, showing 1912–13 extension (left), 1927 entrance, and 1977 expansion into former Dental Hospital premises.

Below right: David E. Owen, the Director who strongly encouraged the development of public programmes and temporary exhibitions, at his retirement presentation, September 1976.

15

was Director for nearly two decades from 1957, was particularly energetic in this regard, instituting regular lectures and workshops, and encouraging the development of temporary exhibitions, including a memorable one displaying samples of moon rock in 1969 just two months after they had been collected from the lunar surface. He also oversaw the development of guidebooks, a schools loans service, and an aquarium with live fish and reptiles.

Whilst there was a further extension of the Museum into space in the old Dental School in 1977 to provide office and storage accommodation, the next major development in the physical appearance of the building occurred from 1994–2003. The Director Tristram Besterman and his team developed and delivered a scheme designed by Manchester-based Ian Simpson Architects to transform the facilities in the Museum, which were then outdated in terms of the needs of modern audiences, from disabled access to standards of display. In total over £20 million was raised from a variety of sources, and by the completion of the final phase in 2003, the Museum had a new entrance providing level access from a newly created courtyard, into a new entrance hall with a modern shop, a dedicated temporary exhibition space, a café (for the first time), and a hands-on Discovery Centre. New lifts were installed to make access easier, and some galleries were redisplayed. Behind the scenes, new labs, offices and meeting spaces were created, and modern storage facilities for the collections were built.

In more recent years, the priorities have been to redisplay the galleries which were not part of that

Right: The new Museum's entrance opened in 2003. The Manchester Museum has an unbroken record of providing free admission to its gallery displays and facilities since it first opened its doors in 1890.

> "*I love the Museum. It's good that admission is free.*"
>
> Museum visitor

The University of Manchester
The Manchester Museum

MANCHESTER 1824

Opening Times:
Tuesday-Saturday 10am-5pm
Sunday, Monday & Bank Holidays 11am-4pm
Last admission 30 minutes before closing
Admission Free

Left: View of the 'Living Worlds' gallery.

Below: Terracotta figurine of a woman and a sedan chair. From Hawara. Roman period, 30 BC–395 AD.

Living Worlds

'Living Worlds' opened in 2011 as a major overhaul of the old classificatory 'Mammals Gallery', transforming it into a new type of natural history gallery that encourages visitors to consider their own relationships with nature. Instead of showing the natural world as classified and unchanging, it shows nature as dynamic, and intextricably affected by human impact. Working with innovative Belgian design firm villa eugénie in their first museum commission, the Museum's team divided the gallery into a series of themes, each treated in a unique way. Some displays relate to particular scientific and environmental topics, while others relate to particular human relationships with nature. This approach is based on an acknowledgement that each visitor has their own views of nature, so that most people should find something that they can connect with. Carefully selected objects and additional materials are beautifully presented and lit to engage with people's emotions. A mounted crane and a piece of rubble from Hiroshima are surrounded by a thousand origami cranes to illustrate the story of a girl who tried, with her friends, to overcome severe illness following the nuclear explosion by folding cranes to make her wish come true. A human skeleton is surrounded by skulls and skeletons of apes and monkeys to emphasise the family connections that we have with other animals. A display case is fitted out like an apartment to explore how we use natural materials in our everyday lives. Each display is accompanied by a panel of text written by an expert from the University explaining their interest in the topic. Detailed information is provided on a dedicated smartphone app which continues to develop, with suggestions of activities to get involved in and places to find out more information.

capital scheme, and to improve engagement with visitors. The new 'Living Worlds' gallery opened in 2011, followed by the three 'Ancient Worlds' galleries in 2012, with 'Nature's Library' (a gallery about encyclopaedic collections and why museums have them) and the vivarium redisplay coming in 2013. At the same time, as later sections show, through government funding to support regional museums, more staff have been employed to work with schools, undertake community outreach, and diversify the Museum's audiences. As a result, visitor numbers have increased to around 350,000 a year – the highest in the history of the Museum – and the demographic composition reflects that of the overall population in many ways.

> "*Brilliant! So great that we have such a fab museum on our doorstep.*"
>
> Museum visitor

One of the key contributions to this considerable increase in visitor numbers has been the programme of temporary exhibitions. In recent years the Museum has experimented with a variety of different approaches to engage visitors with collections in new ways. The 'Lindow Man' exhibition, for example, explored the locally discovered bog body through the stories of eight people who had some kind of association with him, including the peat-cutter who discovered him and the forensic pathologist who examined him. The exhibition 'Charles Darwin: Evolution of a Scientist' explored Darwin's ideas in the form of a graphic novel illustrated with Museum specimens, while 'Breed: The British and their Dogs' presented academic research on the history of Victorian dog breeding through the stories of six key breeds that were thought to encapsulate certain British values.

Work with artists has been a key feature of the exhibition programme, from the 'Alchemy' series of artist research fellowships that resulted in some extraordinary artworks produced in response to the collections, to the 'we are extInked' exhibition of photographs of individuals who had volunteered to be tattooed with a rare or endangered animal and become an ambassador for the species (see p. 142).

At the same time, exhibitions have been an excellent way of introducing some of the University's academic research to wider audiences, from Alan

Above: The temporary exhibition 'Lindow Man' (19 April 2008 – 19 April 2009) won several awards for its innovative approach to display.

18

Below: 'Wild Britain', an exhibition of photographs by leading photographer Ben Hall (July 2006 – August 2007), showed many of the animals in the Museum's collections in their natural settings.

Turing's work on morphogenesis (how shape and pattern in nature are determined) or Grafton Elliot Smith's early 19th century work on Ancient Egyptian populations through analysis of large-scale cemetery excavations.

Fundamentally, the Manchester Museum is a university museum, and so it continues to play a crucial role in the teaching of students, and in the facilitation of research. However, it has always had a hugely important public role, both acting as a friendly 'front door' to a university and providing an educational and inspirational experience to a wide audience in the region and beyond. It is this combination of the academic and the popular which makes the Manchester Museum so distinctive amongst UK museums.

Hidden treasures

Archaeology is… a vast fiendish jigsaw invented by the devil as an instrument of tantalising torment.

Paul Bahn (1989)

Tales from ancient worlds

Even if, to take Paul Bahn's definition of archaeology, many of the pieces of evidence that constitute the jigsaw are missing, the Manchester Museum archaeology collection offers wide coverage of many of the peoples, civilisations and cultures of the ancient world, and features a significant number of objects of regional, national and international importance. It has been the subject of an impressive record of academic research stretching from William Boyd Dawkins' work at Creswell Crags during the 1870s to John Prag and Richard Neave's work on facial reconstruction in the 1980s. The collection is also a wonderful resource with which to explore how our understanding of the past has developed over the last century and a half.

When the first curator of the Manchester Museum, William Boyd Dawkins (1837–1929), rationalised the collections transferred from the Manchester

Ancestors' plough tools

Perhaps some of the simplest yet most intriguing objects in the Manchester Museum archaeology collection are the early medieval plough pebbles from Holderness in East Yorkshire. Plough pebbles are small ovoid pieces of hard stone (typically quartzite) that were inserted into the surface of a wooden plough in order to protect it from abrasion. They were a cheap alternative to using iron. The stones became worn over time and developed distinctive facets with lots of scratches. From time to time they fell out of the plough and remained in the soil to be picked up many years later during archaeological fieldwork. A number of wooden ploughs complete with stones inserted in them have been found in bogs in Denmark. A wooden fragment with plough pebbles from excavations at Whithorn in Scotland was dated to the 7th century AD. It is very likely that the Morfitt family of Atwick in East Yorkshire gave the plough pebbles to Professor William Boyd Dawkins early in the 20th century. Dawkins corresponded with William Morfitt and identified animal bones that the family collected from sites in Holderness in East Yorkshire. He also

visited the Morfitts at their home at Charlotte's Cottage in Atwick. The literature often refers to the discovery of plough pebbles in Lincolnshire and Yorkshire, but the Holderness examples seem to have been overlooked. That may be because anything associated with William and his sons was regarded as slightly suspect after a rather unpleasant controversy involving some prehistoric barbed bone points they had found in Holderness.

Left: Early medieval plough pebbles from Holderness in East Yorkshire.

Natural History Society Museum to Owens College, archaeology was already represented. Dawkins, though a geologist by training (see chapter 5), had a passionate interest in cave archaeology, and carried out excavations at Creswell Crags in Derbyshire with the Revd John Magens Mello and Thomas Heath during the 1870s. He was widely regarded as the authority on the subject, and his book *Cave Hunting* was published in 1874. Dawkins' thinking was influenced by Darwin's theory of evolution by natural selection. He arranged the new displays of the Manchester Museum according to evolutionary principles, starting with rocks and minerals on the ground floor and leading up through the various kingdoms of plant and animal life to Man, thought to be the most evolved form of life. The stone tools were crucial in showing how human beings had evolved over time. The identification of prehistoric flint-working industries was an important feature of Dawkins' work and that of his successor J. Wilfrid Jackson (1880–1978) and helps to explain why the Museum has such extensive prehistoric lithics collections today.

Above: A group of eoliths, or 'dawnstones', collected by Benjamin Harrison from the Kent Plateau.

Below right: Palaeolithic flint Font Robert point from Pinhole Cave, Creswell Crags, Derbyshire, dating from about 29,000 BC.

Below: Late Bronze Age hoard from the River Ribble consisting of bronze socketed axes, two palstaves, and a chisel. The metalwork was in the collection of Thomas Barritt of Manchester.

Dawkins cultivated networks of contacts amongst flint collectors on the Pennines, men such as William Henry Sutcliffe, William Parker and Francis Buckley. Dawkins and local enthusiasts took part in the contemporary debate about eoliths or 'dawnstones'. Whilst some enthusiasts classed them as the earliest prehistoric artefacts found in North Western Europe, Dawkins and others argued they were part of the natural world. The archaeology collection has many boxes of eoliths, including some from Benjamin Harrison of Ightham in Kent, who was one of the leading exponents of such 'dawnstones'. The collection also includes forgeries of flint artefacts, including some made by the notorious Edward Simpson, alias 'Flint Jack', who made a living by selling his fake

objects to museums and private collectors. Dorothy Garrod (1892–1968), the first woman to hold the Professorship of Archaeology at the University of Cambridge, gave stone tools from French cave sites, as well as Tabun and Skhul in Palestine, during the 1930s. She is a rare exception to the predominance of men in archaeology at this time. A. Leslie Armstrong (1879–1958) continued the work at Creswell Crags during the 1920s, and the Manchester Museum is one of a number of institutions holding material from this important Palaeolithic site. A flint Font Robert point excavated by Armstrong and dating from around 29,000 BC is a well-preserved and rare example left by a member of a band of prehistoric hunter-gatherers during a warm spell at the height of the last glaciation. The later 19th- and earlier 20th-century lithic collections retain their significance, and during the 1970s the stone axes were sampled by researchers for the Implement Petrology Scheme. Sections of many of the axes were analysed to create distribution maps showing how far the axes travelled from the source rock, thus revealing extensive prehistoric trading networks.

Dawkins and Jackson's interest in prehistory manifested itself in other ways. Wilfrid Jackson made a public appeal to trace a hoard of late Bronze Age axeheads from the River Ribble once in the collection of Thomas Barritt (1743–1820), the antiquary of Georgian Manchester. This significant collection was sadly dispersed after the death of the owner. The Lawson-Tancred family responded to Jackson's appeal and the Museum now has this significant hoard in its prehistoric metalwork collection. Dawkins also collected material from across the United Kingdom, and gave some beautifully preserved

Iron Age metalwork, including a slave gang chain from Bigbury Camp in Kent, to the collection (see also Expert Spotlight on p. 33).

It is surprising, given the popularity of the Egyptology galleries at the Manchester Museum, that the Museum Committee was initially inclined to turn down local textile merchant Jesse Howarth's generous offer to donate his Egyptology collection. From the early 20th century onwards, once resistance to collecting Egyptology had been overcome, the Museum began to acquire ancient Greek and Roman material. By the 1970s John Boardman, Reader in Classical Archaeology at the University of Oxford, could say of Manchester that 'outside Oxbridge it is the largest Greek and Roman University collection in the country... it offers a good representation of all major classes of pottery and other objects'. The foundation for this new collecting initiative was William Sharp Ogden's donation of antiquities during the 1920s, which enabled what was then a new section of Pre-Classical and Classical Archaeology to be established within the archaeology collection. The exhibits arranged in geographical groups illustrated many of the characteristic features of Mediterranean and Western civilizations in a chronological sequence from the Bronze Age of Cyprus, Crete and Mycenae through the early Greek and classical periods to the Etruscan and Roman cultures.

During the 1930s and 1940s interest in Classics at the University was stimulated by Professor T.B.L. Webster (1905–74). Webster taught in the Classics Department of the University, published papers about the vases in the Museum collection and helped rearrange the Museum displays. Miss A.E.F. Barlow gave some very fine pieces of Greek pottery and a Corinthian mirror. One of the most notable specimens purchased at auction by the Museum is an ancient Greek Red Figure amphora or storage jar by the Berlin Painter dating from the first half of the 5th century BC. It features a scene from Greek mythology. When the hero Herakles visited Pholos, one of the centaurs, he was entertained with food and wine. The other centaurs smelt the wine and joined the party, but drank too much,

Above: Iron Age iron slave gang chain from a hillfort at Bigbury, Kent. The slave chain held up to six captives. It is still in working order and has been successfully demonstrated using University of Manchester archaeology students!

Left: Fine ancient Greek Corinthian mirror dating from about 540 BC presented by Miss A.E.F. Barlow. It shows the goddess Aphrodite in Ionian costume with two winged figures representing Eros on her shoulders.

> *"It's fantastic holding something real that is thousands or millions of years old."*
>
> Museum visitor

Below: Etruscan cinerary urn, dating from 150–125 BC. The lid shows a garlanded man reclining. On a frieze on the side of the urn is an intriguing battle scene in which a woman is about to throw an offering tray of fruit at one of the warriors. This may represent the story of Orestes and Pylades in Tauris attacked by the soldiers of King Thoas.

and in the brawl which followed Herakles killed many of them with his club. A storage jar like this was used to bring wine to a symposium, or drinking party. The Gayer Anderson brothers donated a large collection of Greco-Roman terracottas, including figurines of gods, human heads, animals and lamps. The Museum's collection of Etruscan antiquities expanded significantly with the arrival of material transferred from the Wellcome Trust during the early 1980s. A fine Etruscan sarcophagus was transferred to the Museum from Moyse's Hall, Bury St Edmunds. Other notable Classical antiquities include a fine bronze Corinthian helmet and a bronze figurine of Hermes holding a goat.

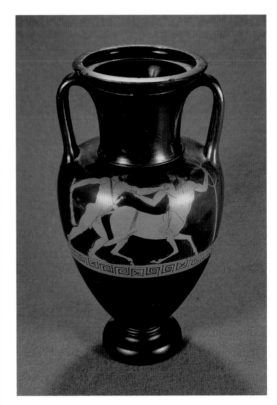

Above: Ancient Greek Red Figure amphora, or storage jar, by the Berlin Painter (working c.500–c.460 BC).

called environmental archaeology and gave some of the first palaeobotany samples from Roman Manchester to the Museum. Sadly many of the first Roman objects to be discovered in Manchester were dispersed. The Museum currently exhibits two altars from Manchester kindly lent by the Ashmolean Museum and the Manchester Art Gallery. In 2008 the Museum acquired a Roman altar found during excavations in advance of development at the junction of Chester Road and Greater Jackson Street. It was dedicated by Aelius Victor 'to the German Mother Goddesses of the Hanenfates and other peoples'. Presumably Victor was a German or had served in Germany prior to his posting to the province of Britannia.

Another local discovery, this time of a rather grisly nature, is the head of Worsley Man. Found in a peat bog in 1958, it was at first suspected to be the head of a modern murder victim, and a police investigation was launched. Once the coroner had established that it was ancient the head went into storage in a pathology lab. Following the discovery of the more intact 'bog body' of Lindow Man in 1984, archaeologists began to appreciate the significance of the head of Worsley Man, which was recovered and transferred to the Manchester Museum. Research similar to that carried out on the body of Lindow Man revealed that Worsley Man too had met a violent death. Radiocarbon dating suggests that he died in the early 2nd century AD. A facial reconstruction by Dr John Prag, former Keeper of Archaeology at the Manchester Museum, and Dr Richard Neave of the University's Art in Medicine section, brought Worsley Man vividly to life (see image on p. 22). Other human remains of research interest in the collection include Neolithic skeletal material from sites in Wales and bones from a 'Dark Age' battlefield site near Chester (see text box on p. 31).

Left: Roman stone altar set up by Aelius Victor to commemorate the mother goddesses of the German tribe of the Hanenfates and other peoples. Found in the centre of Manchester, it may date from the later 2nd century AD.

In addition to Classical material from the Mediterranean, Romano-British antiquities from Manchester and the North West were acquired for the collection. Charles Roeder (1856–1903) and his daughter were pioneers in what would now be

The Manchester word-square

Amongst the objects found during the excavation of the vicus, or civilian settlement, attached to the Roman fort of Manchester was a broken piece of pottery from a storage jar, or amphora, with an incomplete Latin inscription. The letters were part of a word-square, or palindrome, of which a number of complete examples are known from elsewhere in Roman Britain and other parts of the Roman Empire, including Pompeii in Italy and Dura Europos in Syria. The five words ROTAS OPERA TENET AREPO SATOR read the same forwards and backwards, and up and down. When rearranged the letters form the words 'pater noster', or 'Our Father', the first words of the Lord's prayer. Only A and O, or alpha and omega, the first and last letters of the Greek alphabet remain unused, suggesting that the word-square has Christian significance, because Jesus said 'I am the beginning and I am the end.' Believers used the inscription to advertise their presence in a community at times when the Roman authorities were persecuting Christianity. Careful excavation enabled the layer in which the word-square was found to be dated to the early 180s AD, making this potentially the earliest evidence of Christianity in northern Britain. However, some archaeologists have suggested that this is too early in date, and that the word-square may simply be evidence of a Roman pastime or leisure activity akin to completing modern puzzles like Sudoku. It was only later that the word-square acquired its Christian significance. Its presence in Manchester need not be evidence of Christianity.

Left: Word-square, or palindrome, from Roman Manchester. This may be the earliest evidence of Christianity in northern Britain.

The finds from Professor G.D.B. Jones' excavations in the centre of Manchester in the 1970s are one of the largest components of the archaeology collection. One of the most intriguing discoveries was the Manchester word-square (see text box on p. 29). Equally fascinating is a fragmentary Roman military diploma from Ravenglass in Cumbria. It was found by metal-detectorists and reported to the Museum. Whilst the name of the recipient remains unknown, it would appear that he was recruited from near Baalbek in Syria and joined units from the garrison of Roman Britain sent to suppress the Jewish revolt led by Bar Kochba during the 130s AD. This discovery was the start of a trickle of metal-detected finds reported through the Portable Antiquities Scheme or as treasure items from which the Museum archaeology collection has benefited. In recent years the Museum has purchased a silver snake bracelet and a small hoard of Roman silver coins from the Greater Manchester region in this way.

The Museum's relatively modest funds for purchasing antiquities were boosted significantly by the Lancashire and Cheshire Antiquarian Fund set up thanks to the generosity of Dr J.T. D'Ewart

(1872–1961). This enabled the Museum to purchase a number of antiquities at auction during the 1950s and 1960s. These include the beautiful Bronze Age gold wrist clasps, or armillae, from Malpas in Cheshire and an Iron Age gold neck ring, or torc, from Burnley, both regarded as treasures of the collection. The identity of the secret benefactor behind the Fund only became public knowledge after D'Ewart's death in 1961.

Above: Fragmentary Roman military diploma from the 150s AD found by metal-detectorists at Ravenglass in Cumbria. Such diplomas were presented to auxiliary soldiers who had served for 25 years in the Roman army. The diploma recorded the granting of Roman citizenship to the soldier concerned in a durable form.

Left: Roman silver snake bracelet found by a metal-detectorist in the Greater Manchester region. Unfortunately the bracelet has been straightened. The original configuration is shown by the bronze example.

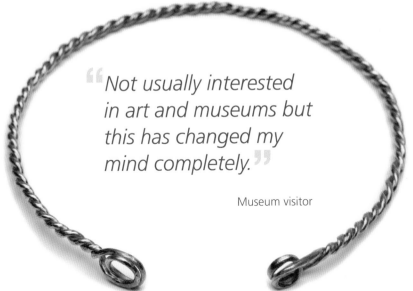

Above: Two Bronze Age gold armillae, or wrist clasps, from Malpas, Cheshire. The twisting of the gold required great skill. It is very likely that they were made in Ireland, where important gold deposits were exploited in prehistory.

Right: Iron Age gold torc, or neck-ring, from Burnley.

New wine from ancient bottles...

The Manchester Museum's archaeology collection features human skeletons from Heronbridge, near Chester, excavated during the early 1930s. Although there was much Roman material on the site, the skeletons appear to be of later date. Radiocarbon dating of two human skeletons excavated more recently from the same site suggests that the remains are of the early medieval period, sometimes referred to as 'the Dark Ages'. There is clear evidence that the individuals, all mature men, died violently. Afterwards the dead were stripped of their belongings and laid to rest with some degree of care in burial pits. This dating evidence, together with extensive evidence of trauma inflicted by edged weapons, leads to the conclusion that the men were casualties of the battle of Chester (about 616 AD). In this battle a Northumbrian army led by King Aethelfrith defeated the Northern Welsh Britons. The encounter is described by Bede in his *Ecclesiastical History of the English People* (II, 2). In this account, Aethelfrith ordered his men to cut down Christian monks who were present at the battle and praying for a British victory. Professor Nick Higham of the University of Manchester has argued that we should not take this at face value, because Bede was writing with a religious agenda in mind. Even if the skeletons are not those of Christian monks, a connection with this Dark Age confrontation is very likely. The material has attracted considerable interest from forensic archaeologists and palaeopathologists.

Above: Two human skulls from Heronbridge. One of the skulls shows cut-marks inflicted by an edged weapon such as a sword.

31

As attitudes to the purchase of material at auction changed, Museum funds were redirected to support archaeological fieldwork in the eastern Mediterranean and the Middle East. In return for a modest subscription the Museum received a share of the finds. In this way the Museum acquired material from Qasr Ibrim in Egypt, Tel Rifa'at and Tell es-Sweyhat in Syria, Lachish (Israel), Tell Abu Hureyra (Syria), Udruh (Jordan) and other sites. This complements finds from some of William Flinders Petrie's excavations. Though famous for his painstaking excavations of ancient Egyptian sites, Petrie (1853–1942) also worked in Palestine, and the Museum has finds from Tell Fara, Gerar and Tell el Ajjul (Old Gaza). One of the most valuable artefacts in the Museum's collection is an ancient Assyrian slab with carved bas-relief of a winged deity and a cuneiform inscription from Nimrud in northern Iraq. This is said to have been acquired during the 1840s from Henry Rawlinson (1810–95) and Austen Henry Layard (1817–94), founding fathers of Mesopotamian archaeology and the study of cuneiform writing. The Nimrud inscription was presented in 1926. The Museum's collection of cuneiform tablets, a significant proportion given by the brothers of Walter Behrens (1862–1913), is considered to be one of the larger collections outside London.

Right: Carved stone panel from Nimrud, Mesopotamia (Iraq), with inscription in cuneiform or wedge-shaped characters. It was set up by Asshurnasirpal II King of Assyria (883–859 BC) in honour of the god Asshur and records the conquest of nations as far as the Mediterranean.

Archaeology

As a lecturer in the University I regularly make use of the archaeology collections in the Manchester Museum. I have a specialist interest in the Iron Age, so having access to high-quality material such as the metalwork from Bigbury in Kent is a great resource for academic research as well as for teaching students. I believe passionately that there really isn't any substitute so far as students are concerned to handling the real thing: the thrill of holding these 2,000-year-old objects never diminishes, and increases your respect for prehistoric people. There are always new questions to ask! The Museum – and the generosity of its curators and gallery staff – is what makes Manchester a very special place to study archaeology. The Bigbury material includes wrought-iron weapons, agricultural tools, feasting equipment and decorated horse or chariot-gear. These objects tell us much about Iron Age life: the importance of farming, the value of craft knowledge, the significance of horsemanship and martial display, and the use of hospitality to demonstrate status and cement alliances. Yet the most iconic objects – such as a slave chain with six neck-rings and two sets of manacles – also shed light on a darker side of society. Slaves were a major British export by the early Roman period, but high status captives may also have been shackled and humiliated to enhance a rival's power. These were a people without written history, so it is only through the things that they made that we can gain a glimpse of life in Britain at the cusp of the Roman invasion. This prestigious, highly prized metalwork will, I feel sure, continue to inspire and haunt visitors, students and academics – perhaps even poets and artists – for generations to come.

Melanie Giles
Lecturer in Archaeology
University of Manchester

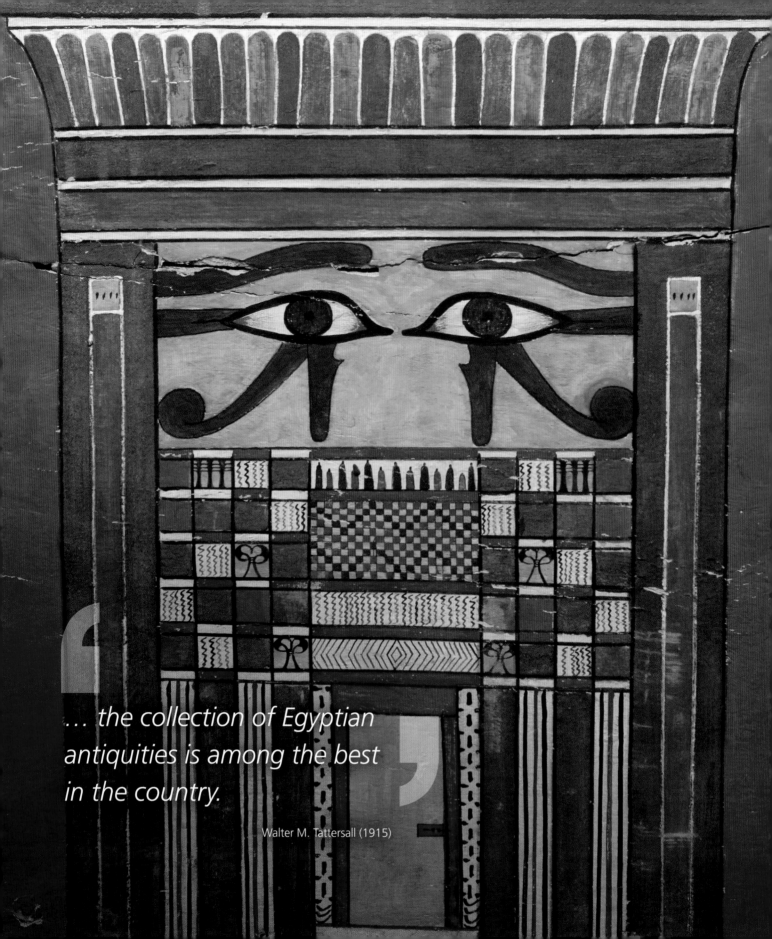

… the collection of Egyptian antiquities is among the best in the country.

Walter M. Tattersall (1915)

Living and dying under the pharaohs

02

Opposite: Eye panel from the box coffin of Nakht-ankh.

Right: Coffins and mummy of the singer Asru, Western Thebes, Twenty-fifth Dynasty (*c.*750–656 BC).

Ancient Egypt appears remarkably familiar to us, both because the Egyptians intended for so many of their creations to last for eternity, and due to the exceptional preservation conditions of Egypt's dry climate, we are permitted an intimate glimpse into life – and death – thousands of years ago. Manchester's collection of objects from Egypt and Sudan gives a clearer picture than most, illustrating both everyday life and preparations for the afterlife.

The Manchester Museum's wide range of objects from ancient Egypt and Sudan arguably form our most popular collective attraction. The collection contains over 15,000 artefacts, making it the fifth largest in the United Kingdom. In 1825, a mummy and two coffins were first to enter what was then the Manchester Natural History Society collection, when they were donated by Robert and William Garratt. These belonged to a woman named Asru, a singer in the temple of the god Amun during the Twenty-fifth Dynasty (*c.*750–656 BC), and probably originated from Luxor. The mummy had already been unwrapped, as this was a fashionable entertainment

> " *Asru is amazing. It is great to be so close to history.* "

Museum visitor

of the time. This attitude towards ancient Egyptian 'curiosities' was typical in the 18th and 19th centuries.

The development of such a comprehensive Egyptology collection in Manchester is thanks in large part to the generosity of one man, Jesse Haworth (1835–1921). Haworth was a wealthy local industrialist whose interest in ancient Egypt appears to have been sparked by reading Amelia Edwards' account of her travels, *A Thousand Miles up the Nile*, published in 1877. Edwards was an early and energetic champion of British fieldwork in Egypt, especially through her writing, and she founded the Egypt Exploration Fund (now Society). Some time after his first trip to Egypt in 1880, Haworth began a correspondence with the author. She encouraged him to channel his enthusiasm for Egyptology into financial support for the work of an up-and-coming archaeologist: William Matthew Flinders Petrie (1853–1942).

Petrie's archaeological work in Egypt was extensive in scope and pioneering in its systematic, scientific approach. Along with another benefactor, London businessman H. Martyn Kennard, Howarth was Petrie's major excavation sponsor between 1887 and 1892. As a result of their support, Howarth and Kennard each personally acquired a significant portion of Petrie's finds, which were in turn largely bequeathed to the Manchester Museum. This double philanthropy was to be of great importance, because it meant that a large number of objects in the Manchester collection

A gem from Riqqeh

Known today as the Riqqeh Pectoral after the site at which it was discovered, this small, ornate chest ornament, worn on a necklace, is a highlight of the Manchester collection. The piece was created using a technique termed cloisonné, in which separate gold sections are filled with semi-precious stones. Lapis lazuli (dark blue), carnelian (red) and turquoise (blue/green) give the pectoral its colourful appearance and gem-like lustre. The piece was found in association with two other items, each in the form of a king's name: Senuseret II (Khakheperre) and Senuseret III (Khakaure). It can therefore be reliably dated to the second half of the Twelfth Dynasty (c.1900–1840 BC). The archaeological context of the pectoral was a dramatic one. Reginald Engelbach was excavating in a cemetery at el-Riqqeh, near the entrance to the Faiyum lake region. At the bottom of a deep tomb shaft, Engelbach discovered an apparently intact chamber, the roof of which had collapsed in antiquity. At the centre of the chamber was a coffin containing a mummy – but with the arm-bones of another body lying on top of it. Within the wrappings several items of jewellery, including the pectoral, had apparently been dislodged. All the evidence suggests that a robber must have been crushed in the act of rifling for valuables when the roof collapsed.

Above: The Riqqeh Pectoral.

Right: The Egyptian Gallery shortly after it opened in 1912.

came from a well-recorded archaeological context, allowing a much more detailed understanding of them than if they had been bought on the antiquities market.

As the home to a rapidly expanding collection of Egyptian objects, as well as a burgeoning interest in Egyptology, Manchester attracted both Amelia Edwards and Flinders Petrie to give regular lectures in the city. In 1913 the Manchester Egyptian and Oriental Society passed a resolution to host a series of lectures in the Museum, beginning a tradition of providing educational resources and fostering enthusiasm among non-specialists that continues to the present day.

A substantial donation from Haworth enabled the construction of a dedicated extension to house the Egyptian collection, which opened on 30 October 1912 in the presence of Flinders Petrie. A major refurbishment of the galleries opened in 2012 on the exact centenary of the original opening. Haworth made a further bequest in 1919, and after his death the Museum received £30,000 and his private collection of Egyptian antiquities. Marianne Haworth, Jesse's widow, opened another extension in November 1927 to provide much-needed storage and exhibition space (see p. 15 for further details).

"Fantastic place to learn about the Egyptians."

Museum visitors

Most significantly, Petrie brought to light not just the contents of tombs but aspects of everyday life in Egyptian towns. Petrie's investigations of Kahun, a settlement purpose-built to house the pyramid-builders of King Senusret II (c.1877–1870 BC), were groundbreaking. Here Petrie uncovered and recorded plentiful evidence for day-to-day life in the town, including personal religious practices and the trades in which the town's inhabitants were engaged. Life at the royal court during the Eighteenth Dynasty (c.1550–1350 BC) is illustrated by finds from the site of a harem palace at Gurob and Amarna, the city constructed by Akhenaten to worship the sun-disk. Both of these elite communities favoured objects with decoration that celebrated the natural world. The large proportion of artefacts from these 'living'

Above: A tool kit, Kahun, Twelfth Dynasty (c.1991–1783 BC).

Left: Pottery incense burner, Kahun, Middle Kingdom (c.2025–1650 BC).

Above: Blue faience vessel with duck decoration, Gurob, New Kingdom (c.1400–1200 BC).

Above right: Inlays from Amarna, New Kingdom (c.1340 BC).

Right: Pottery bowl, with white cross-lined (c-ware) decoration and hippos around the rim, Predynastic Period (Nagada I) (c.4400–3500 BC).

sites is a key strength of the Manchester collection, one of the most representative in the world for such material. Thanks to these rich holdings, the Museum has been uniquely placed to challenge the persistent stereotype of the ancient Egyptians as morbidly focused only on death.

Naturally, temple sites and cemeteries appealed to early excavators because they were guaranteed to yield monumental or visually appealing objects to entice benefactors. Petrie was no exception in this regard, and through his intensive investigation of such sites also added to our knowledge of religious and funerary practices. Even seemingly utilitarian pottery vessels found in Egypt's earliest and simplest graves carry some of the culture's most distinctive designs. In particular, the Egyptians' striking use

of animal motifs have always struck a chord with modern museum visitors.

The site of Thebes, modern Luxor, is home to Egypt's most famous cemeteries and has yielded some of the richest funerary equipment. Unfortunately, these often come from uncontrolled digs and so lack the exact provenance characteristic of Petrie's excavations.

Above: Limestone flake, or ostracon, showing a funeral, Western Thebes, New Kingdom (*c.*1557–1069 BC).

Right: Gilded and painted plaster mummy mask, Western Thebes, early New Kingdom (*c.*1550 BC).

Also from Thebes come some objects of low intrinsic value, but perhaps the most intriguing function of any in the collection. At the end of the 19th century, using Haworth/Kennard funds, Petrie's men discovered a Thirteenth Dynasty (*c.*1773–1650 BC) tomb of a practitioner of magic. Along with a box of magico-medical texts written on papyrus, the tomb's contents included ivory protective 'wands' and a figurine of a masked female shown grasping two snakes, perhaps employed in performative magic.

Certain types of objects are very common, and these proved particularly popular with collectors. *Shabti*-figures, of a wide range of types and qualities, are therefore well-represented in the collection. These small, mummiform figures often bear hieroglyphic inscriptions describing their duties as servants for the tomb owner in the afterlife. *Shabtis* are recognisably ancient Egyptian, conveniently portable (and saleable), and therefore often arrived in museums without a

Left: Wooden female figurine, with the face (mask?) of a deity and holding snakes. Thirteenth Dynasty (c. 1773–1650 BC).

Below: Faience shabti, or servant figurine, of man named Horudja, Hawara, Thirtieth Dynasty (380–343 BC).

known archaeological context. One remarkable find of 399 very fine *shabtis* was made by Petrie in the tomb of a Thirtieth Dynasty (380–343 BC) priest named Horudja at Hawara, 58 examples of which are in Manchester. Numbers of such objects in the collection increased when the Egyptian holdings were supplemented from the purchases of collectors, such as Max Robinow (–1900), Sir Henry Wellcome (1853–1936) and Annie Barlow (1863–1941). Before the Egyptian government placed a ban on the export of antiquities from Egypt in the 1980s, the Museum further added to the Egyptology collections by subscribing to more recent excavations such as those

"*I found the mummies quite scary but they fascinated me and now I want to know more about Egyptian history!*"

Museum visitor

Left: Serpentine statuette of an official. Middle Kingdom (c.2025–1650 BC).

Right: Votive mummy of an ibis, Saqqara, Late Period (c.664–30 BC).

of the Egypt Exploration Society at Saqqara, which yielded a last batch of well-provenanced finds.

The Museum has always been at the centre of the study of ancient Egypt in Manchester. Some of the greatest names in Egyptology have advised on the collection: Francis Llewellyn Griffith, founder of the Griffith Institute in Oxford, was Lecturer in Egyptology at the Victoria Manchester University from 1898 until 1908, Thomas Eric Peet (1882–1934) took the role between 1913–28, and the great philologist Sir Alan Gardiner held his only teaching post here between 1912 and 1914. The collection could also draw on expertise from outside

Two half-brothers?

In 1907, an intact tomb was discovered at Deir Rifeh in Middle Egypt. It dated to the second half of the Twelfth Dynasty (c.1900–1783 BC) and contained the burials of two men – Khnum-Nakht and Nakht-Ankh. Each was provided with a brightly painted mummy case within an outer box coffin, along with a small

Below: The inner coffins of Two Brothers.

but fine range of grave goods, including statuettes, model boats and pottery. Hieroglyphic texts indicated that the men were each sons of a local governor and shared the same mother, leading to them being dubbed 'the Two Brothers'. Petrie recognised how important it was that the burial assemblage was complete, and secured special permission for the entire group of objects to be transported to Manchester. The mummies were unwrapped in 1908 by a team of specialists from varied disciplines, led by Margaret Murray. Both mummies were rather poorly preserved, with little flesh left on the bones. Nakht-Ankh had been provided with higher-quality coffins than his brother, as well as a canopic chest, which held his internal organs removed during mummification. Modern scientific examination has shown that Nakht-Ankh suffered from pleurisy and sand pneumoconiosis, which may have caused his death. Furthermore, the brothers' skulls exhibit markedly different racial characteristics, suggesting that if they were genetically related (rather than adoptive) brothers their mother had two different husbands – one of Nubian origin.

Egyptology. Sir Grafton Elliot Smith, Professor of Anatomy at Manchester University, was for example the first scholar to x-ray Egyptian mummies.

Margaret Murray (1863–1963) was one of Petrie's most able students and, although never a paid member of staff at the Manchester Museum, worked on cataloguing the Haworth collection between 1906 and 1908. Most famously, she undertook the study of the remarkable Two Brothers' tomb assemblage. By coordinating a team of specialists to unwrap

the mummy of Khnum-nakht, Murray initiated Manchester's scientific approach to mummified remains, while at the same time satisfying a strong sense of public curiosity. A contemporary spectator recounted: 'The unrolling was witnessed by 500 people and lasted one hour and a half. At the close of the ceremony, members of the audience who wished to have a piece of the mummy wrappings were invited by the Chairman of the meeting to leave their names and addresses.'

Below: Margaret Murray (in pinafore) and assistants, with the mummy of Khnum-nakht (1908).

Murray was the first in a line of female Egyptologists to be associated with the Museum, of whom the most well-known is Rosalie David. David joined the staff as Assistant Keeper for Archaeology in 1972, and subsequently held the title Keeper of Egyptology. She brought research on the Egyptology collection to international attention with her work on the Manchester Mummy Project (see text box on p. 128), and through numerous published works.

One of David's most notable predecessors was Winifred Crompton. She studied Egyptology with Peet at Manchester University, worked originally as the Museum's printer in charge of labels and was appointed the first Assistant Keeper of Egyptology in 1910. For over 20 years Crompton forged ties between the Museum and local society members, encouraged volunteers, and oversaw a programme of lectures and activities for school groups. Manchester is notable for being among the first to use its Egyptian objects to engage with these groups. Continuing community ties are an important reason why the collections remain so popular today.

The face of two worlds

Graeco-Roman mummy portraits are amongst the most evocative images to have come from Egypt. These portraits were painted using an encaustic method, in which pigment is mixed with hot wax and applied directly onto the surface of thin wooden panels. Such panels were attached over the head of the mummy, held in place with bandages around each edge. This practice developed out of the pharaonic tradition of covering the head of the mummy with an idealised image of the deceased. Portrait painting had its roots in Roman traditions, and the portrait panels are the result of cross-fertilisation in the burial customs of Egypt's multicultural society at this time. Painted portraits are attested at sites across Roman Egypt. Most are, however, associated with Hawara, a site in the Faiyum, from where the present example derives. The panels are often referred to as 'Faiyum portraits' because Flinders Petrie discovered over 700 examples in the region. This panel carries a portrait on both sides, one of a youthful man with a coiffure fashionable during the reign of Hadrian, and a rougher (partially erased?) sketch on the reverse perhaps representing a more mature version of the same man. A further panel, perhaps depicting the same man but with a bare chest, indicating athletic vigour, was found broken and bound within the mummy's wrappings. Each depiction represents a different aspect of the deceased's identity, which could potentially survive by being enclosed within the individual's burial.

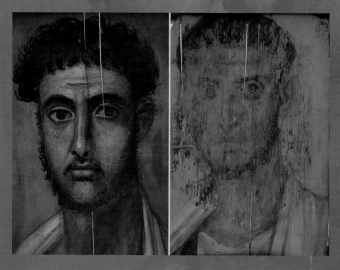

Above: Double-sided portrait.

Egyptology

Many of us are fascinated by the world of the ancient Egyptians, yet few of us are able to travel to the land of the pharaohs. The galleries of the Manchester

Museum offer visitors the opportunity to forget the modern world and immerse themselves in the past: to examine a hand-made pot, an intricately decorated coffin or a simple string of beads, and establish a personal link with craft-workers and tomb owners who lived and died beside the Nile many thousands of years ago. That this experience is free of charge and open to all is fantastic. I know from my own experience as a parent that all family members, from the youngest to the oldest, can find something to enjoy within the walls of the Manchester Museum. Watching the level of engagement generated by just one of the artefacts in the collection – a replica of the world-famous Berlin bust of the Egyptian Queen Nefertiti – has prompted me to research the public reception of this bust, and I am currently writing a book on this subject.

I will always be grateful to the Museum for inspiring me in this way. But not everyone is able to visit the Museum in person. As a lecturer who teaches entirely on-line, I have students of all ages and experiences scattered across the globe. As my students are unable to visit Manchester, I have worked with the Museum staff to bring the Manchester collection directly to my students, using a combination of photography, video and web-based resources. Thus, students as far away as Australia, Mexico and Canada have been able to develop a deep-felt connection with the ancient peoples of Egypt and the Sudan, with each other, and with the Manchester Museum itself.

Joyce Tyldesley
Senior Lecturer in Egyptology
University of Manchester

The Mancunian anthropology remains a distinctive school of thought of a weight hardly to be surpassed by other currents in social anthropology or cultural anthropology.

Marian Kempny (2006)

Collecting cultures, making connections

03

Ethnography is the study of all the very many cultures and people found throughout the world. Ethnographic collections contain the different types of objects used and created by these cultures. The Manchester Museum began collecting such objects in 1892 when a Professor Henderson donated what is simply described as a 'stone hache' (axe) from the town of Yercaud in the Shevaroy Hills, India. Henderson's donation coincided with an increasing interest in non-European peoples as the British Empire continued to expand. This expansion stimulated an ambition to prove the superiority of Western culture, map the distribution of humankind, and preserve non-European cultural traditions from presumed extinction. Ethnographic objects were used to fulfill this ambition with museums acquiring a regular supply from missionaries, merchants and soldiers. As the Empire contracted in the later 20th century, correspondingly a greater understanding of non-European cultures emerged. Ethnographic collections began to be developed in collaboration with communities and supported with documentary material including photographs, field notes and books. The Living Cultures collection charts this intellectual transition; it began as the sporadic acquisition of unfamiliar objects eventually becoming an internationally recognised collection primarily used to promote understanding between cultures. Today the collection has grown to over 18,000 objects from Africa, the Americas, Asia and Oceania.

Professor Henderson may have donated the first ethnographic object but it was R.D. Darbishire's (1826–1908) donation which formed the nucleus of the collection. Darbishire was a local solicitor, trustee of Owens College (University of Manchester), and member of the Manchester Natural History Society. Most importantly in this case he was a prolific collector of ethnographic objects, with a particular taste for those from the Arctic and pre-Hispanic Peru. In 1904–5 he made his first major donation of 92 pieces of pre-Hispanic Peruvian pottery from tomb sites including Piura and Cuzco, amongst others. He eventually donated over 700 objects to the steadily growing collection, amongst which 19th

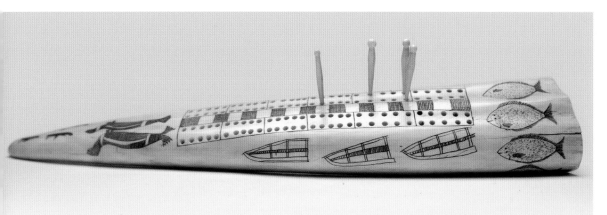

Left: Inuit cribbage board carved from a walrus tusk, c. 19th century, Aleutian Islands, Alaska, USA.

Below: An intricately decorated Aboriginal parrying shield carved from wood, c. 19th century, Victoria, Australia.

Bottom: Hatchet-shaped boomerang made from wood, c. 19th century, Australia.

century Inuit ivory carvings from Alaska are some of the most captivating. One of the most recognisable pieces is a walrus tusk carved into a cribbage board from the Aleutian Islands, Alaska.

A contemporary of Darbishire, Charles Heape (1848–1926), made an even greater contribution to the collection. Heape was a local businessman and landowner from the town of Rochdale. He worked for the Strines Calico Printing Company from 1876 and by 1903 he was director of the Calico Printers Association. Heape had a passion for all things ethnographic and was a member of several distinguished scientific societies, the most notable being the Royal Geographical Society and the Anthropological Institute. Inspired by encounters with Aboriginal Australians as a child, and a gift of Aboriginal objects from his uncle, he collected ethnographic objects over an extensive 40-year period. Remarkably, the clubs, boomerangs and shields from Victoria in the Museum may well be those given to him by his uncle in the late 19th century, each one ergonomically crafted and some with intricate decoration. His collections of Aboriginal, Maori and South Pacific objects are of international importance and rarity. In 1922 he offered the Museum the whole of his collection,

> "*I was really impressed with the space and liked what you guys are doing up there. It felt like a good space to be – challenging and open.*"
>
> Museum colleague from New Zealand

Left: A ceremonial paddle carved from wood, c.19th century, Raivavae, Austral Islands, French Polynesia.

Below: A Maori hei-tiki/ornamental pendant carved from greenstone/pounamu, 19th century, New Zealand.

which amounted to some 2,821 objects, and a copy of his co-authored *An album of the weapons, tools, ornaments, articles of dress of the natives of the Pacific Islands / drawn and described from examples in public & private collections in England.* Surprisingly, he did not offer his collection to his local Rochdale Museum but chose the Manchester Museum because of its already extensive galleries and ethnology teaching programme. The University of Manchester demonstrated their thanks to Heape by bestowing on him an honorary degree of Master of Science in 1924.

Mancunian collectors and societies depended on regional and Empire-wide vendors. Late 19th-century Manchester was a bustling industrial metropolis specialising in the manufacture of cotton merchandise and associated industries. This economic success was accompanied by intellectual enterprise and individuals, such as Darbishire and Heape, and learned societies, such as the Manchester Society for the Promotion of Natural History, sought to acquire the most splendid ethnographic objects. In 1847 the Society acquired a Burmese gilt sculpture of Buddha Siddhārtha Gautama direct from the vendor, an Edward Higgin of Calcutta. When it arrived in Manchester it was reported to be the largest of its kind in the UK (see image on p. 46). The Society sold it at auction in 1868 and it was bought by Salford Museum. Salford Museum eventually transferred it to the Manchester Museum in 1989 following an earlier exchange of 1,675 non-European ethnographic objects for Manchester's English and European folk life collection in 1969–70.

In the early 20th century the reputation of the burgeoning Manchester Museum ethnographic collection began to spread, and non-Manchester-based collectors became increasingly keen to contribute. One such collector was R.W. Lloyd

An iron dragon (**above**) and an iron praying mantis (**right**) made by Miochin Munetane, Edo Period (1600–1868), Japan.

(1868–1958; see photo on p. 91), who was a successful businessman specialising in lithograph printing and bleaching. Lloyd was born in Lancashire but as a child moved to Clapham, London, as a result of his parents separating. Although London-based he pursued business interests in North West England, specifically Manchester, and as a collector maintained a strong relationship with the Manchester Museum. Upon his death he generously bequeathed over 1,000 Japanese objects, including late 17th- to early 19th-century swords, wood carvings, and lacquer work. The most significant objects include several iron articulated models, including a dragon and a praying mantis, made by Miochin Munetane during the Edo period, 1600–1868. The earliest object is a 'tachi', a long sword, made by Sadanaga, a smith from Bizen Provence, Japan, c.1360. As a former director of auction house Christie's it is unsurprising that Lloyd was capable of acquiring such magnificent objects.

Below: A steel tachi/ long sword made by the blacksmith Sadanaga, c.1360, Bizen Provence, Japan.

Elsie McDougall Collection

Eminent Central American ethnologist Elsie McDougall (1883–1961) made a generous donation of textiles, weaving and spinning equipment and photographs in 1947. This donation greatly enhanced the already reputable collection of ethnographic textiles. Part of the donation was transferred to the Museum's sister institution, the Whitworth Art Gallery, in 1961. McDougall was born in the UK but moved to the USA in her 30s. As a self-taught ethnographer she was fascinated with the traditional spinning and weaving techniques of the indigenous people of Guatemala and Mexico. Throughout the 1930s she conducted extensive fieldwork documenting methods, capturing images and collecting objects. In her pursuit of authenticity she travelled to particularly remote areas including Hidalgo, central Mexico, where she worked closely with the Otomi people. Her entire collection has been widely distributed amongst ethnographic museums, including the Pitt Rivers Museum at the University of Oxford, the Peabody Museum at Harvard University and the American Museum of Natural History, New York.

Above left: A stone spindle-whorl and wool for making a felted poncho. 1936. Hidalgo, Mexico.

Left: Yarn dyed with murex dye, 1936, Pacific coast, southern Mexico.

Christian missionaries were extraordinarily industrious in the sale of ethnographic objects. Heape acquired a considerable amount of his collection from missionaries and even recalls an admission on behalf of a missionary of coercing the local populace to produce objects for sale. Not all missionaries sold their collections, but would on occasion bequeath them to museums. The Manchester Museum benefited significantly from missionary activity, particularly in 1977 when the Revd C.K.K. Prosser's (1897–1954) wife donated his collection. Prosser was Rector of Alert Bay, North

Vancouver Island, part of the Church of England Columbia Coast Mission, from 1926–34. A keen photographer, he captured images of Kwakwaka'wakw timber houses, villages, and ceremonies. He collected over 50 objects, of which the Northwest Coast statuettes are of particular importance. One statuette depicts a seated individual reading a book, possibly the Bible, whilst an eagle perches on the reader's head. The wings of the eagle are outstretched in familiar Northwest Coast style, but on the left wing the name 'Charlie James' has been inscribed with the date 'Aug. 12th. 1929' inscribed on the other. Charlie James (1867–1938) was a renowned Kwakwaka'wakw artist, responsible

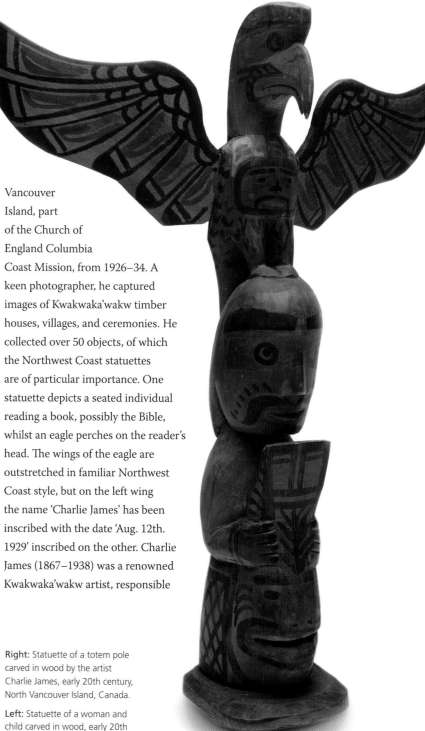

Right: Statuette of a totem pole carved in wood by the artist Charlie James, early 20th century, North Vancouver Island, Canada.

Left: Statuette of a woman and child carved in wood, early 20th century, North Vancouver Island, Canada.

for carving numerous totemic sculptures. Other fascinating statuettes include indigenous depictions of Christ, the crucifixion, and the Virgin Mary with child. These statuettes effectively illustrate the impact of missionary activity as indigenous beliefs and Christianity are seen to merge, a phenomenon called syncretism. Such beautiful objects belie the traumatic effects of religious and cultural conversion.

Prosser's collection is part of a much larger Americas collection at the Manchester Museum, a significant component of which was donated by the Wellcome Trust. The Wellcome Trust was founded by pharmaceutical entrepreneur and renowned collector Sir Henry Wellcome (1853–1936). Wellcome was born in the USA and his childhood familiarity with Native American culture inspired his interest in ethnology, just as Heape's experience in Australia had. Wellcome was a successful businessman, collector and funder of medical innovation. He co-founded a multinational pharmaceutical company, Burroughs Wellcome & Company in 1880, and acquired a truly vast collection, dwarfing that of Darbishire, Heape,

Statuette of the crucifixion (**right**) and a cradle and child (**below**), both carved in wood, early 20th century, North Vancouver Island, Canada.

53

Lloyd, Salford Museum and Prosser combined. In 1926, 1953 and 1981, the Trust, on behalf of the Wellcome Historical Medical Museum, donated parts of this huge collection to the Manchester Museum. A most fascinating piece given by the Trust is an exquisite ceramic spout-and-handle bottle which dates to the Early Nasca culture *c*.300 BC, on the south coast of Peru. It possibly represents a shaman holding a rattle and wearing a wildcat skin headdress.

Like many collectors, including Heape and Lloyd, Wellcome acquired ethnographic objects from existing collections of international repute. Lloyd's donation, for instance, combines parts of other reputable Japanese collections including those of Tomkinson, Behrens, and those displayed at the 1916 Red Cross benefit exhibition. In Wellcome's case he acquired part of Manuel García Elgueta's Mayan collection. Elgueta (1846–1912) was a pioneer of Mayan linguistics and archaeology, and simultaneously a politician, writer and journalist.

Right: Nasca spout-and-handle bottle made from clay, Early Nasca culture (*c*.300), Peru.

Left: Mayan ball court marker carved in stone, Classic period (250–900), Pichiquil, Guatemala.

"Thank you and your staff for the wonderful assistance – and conversation – on my recent visit!"

Professor Norman K. Denzin,
University of Illinois at
Urbana-Champaign, USA

The Archery collection

The Archery collection consists of over 4,000 objects from all over the world. Objects include crossbows from Europe and Asia, composite bows from India and Pakistan, Japanese laminated bows, English longbows, steel bows, thumb rings and arrows. The nucleus of the collection was donated by Ingo Simon in 1946. Simon was fascinated with the development of the bow and spent a considerable period of his life researching it. In his own right he was a skilled archer, and his 1914 flight shot of 462 yards was a world record until 1933. Upon his death in 1964 his wife Erna, herself an accomplished archer and Lady World Champion in 1937, endowed a Trust to the Museum in 1970 to conserve and develop the collection. The Simon Archery Foundation was formed to administer the Trust, which in its inaugural year commissioned Vilma Chiara (Dr Schultz) to acquire archery material from an Amazonian expedition in Brazil. The Foundation's purpose is to acquire archive material and to act as a repository for material relating to the development of archery. Simon was passionate about promoting the significance of archery as he thought it a 'great pity when an art of any sort gets forgotten'.

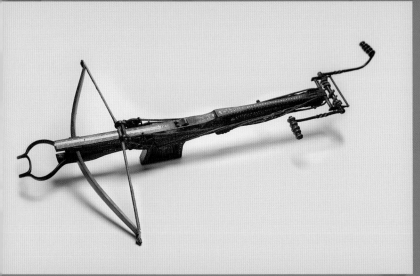

Above: Bolt-shooting crossbow with its windlass and ivory inlay, c. 16th century, Limoges, France.

Below: Mayan head carved in stone, Classic period (250–900), Chalchitán, Guatemala.

He collected extensively in the Huehuetenango region of northwestern Guatemala, and his objects were displayed at the 1893 World's Columbian Exposition in Chicago and the 1894 Mid-Winter Fair in San Francisco. Elgueta studied the people and cultures of the Guatemalan highlands, specifically the K'iche', in an attempt to demonstrate cultural continuity with the pre-Hispanic Maya. The stonework in the collection comes from the important Mayan sites of Pichiquil and Chalchitán, Guatemala, and dates to the Classic period, 250–900. Elgueta's collection has now been widely dispersed, with the California Academy of Sciences, San Francisco, USA, in possession of a very significant piece.

As a university museum, the Manchester Museum benefited by acquiring collections from social anthropologists in the University of Manchester. The Department of Social Anthropology was founded by Max Gluckman in 1949, and has since achieved international repute. In an emerging post-colonial world the Department was committed to social justice, and focused on instances of change

Left: Mursi cow bell/kodo
made from a tortoise shell,
1969–70, Ethiopia.

and conflict within society. This type of social anthropological research became known as the Manchester School, and the work of Dr David Turton exemplifies it. Turton, one-time director of the Department of Social Anthropology, conducted extensive fieldwork in the lower Omo valley of southwestern Ethiopia with the Mursi people, studying the impact of ecological, cultural and political change on the Mursi's traditional way of life. Between 1969 and 1986 he was able to acquire an extensive collection of Mursi ethnographic objects accompanied by photographs and field notes.

Turton's collection is relatively recent, which means the community from which the objects originate is in existence today. However, even those objects within the Living Cultures collection which are seemingly ancient, such as Elgueta's Mayan stonework, still have a cultural connection with descendant communities, either in multicultural Manchester or the country of origin. In the vast majority of cases they are the objects of living people, living communities and living cultures. This relationship between object and ethnicity is explored at the Manchester Museum in an attempt to foster a greater understanding of humankind's cultural similarities and differences. By means of exhibitions, teaching, research and community outreach the collection is stimulating a rich and varied dialogue on this relationship with academics, artists, communities, students and visitors. This exploratory collaboration has been accompanied by a recognition and critique of previous ill-conceived concepts of non-European culture and contentious modes of acquisition at the Museum. Victorian ethnographic orthodoxies have been challenged, and innovative interpretative practices and modes of engagement are continuingly being employed with the collection at their heart.

Living Cultures

As an Aboriginal Australian researcher in the field of museum practice, I've spent the last two years visiting more than 250 museums across five countries undertaking a major international review of significant national keeping places. The Living Cultures programme at the Manchester Museum exemplifies the kind of representation our project has been seeking. They cleverly explore engagement between the community and the museum, inviting meaningful representations and input from the people that make up multicultural Manchester. By exhibiting objects and weaving stories that invoke the past and present communities, they show the visitor a museum and a city that has a relevant and vibrant voice. Our research has indicated that one of the most difficult tasks for contemporary museum spaces is to have the objects in their collection resonate for their visitors. Even the name, Living Cultures, is an indicator of the commitment that the Museum has to understanding that these are not only objects, but also markers of a story that has a contemporary resonance. The Living Cultures programme boldly invites community response to the objects displayed in the galleries, then incorporates these responses into the space. Many museums see this as risky, with a concern that there may be responses that the museum cannot control. But here, the Museum chooses to brave it out, and provide this space for interactions by community members who have an investment in the culture represented. This is extended beyond the walls of the Museum into the realm of social networking – one of the riskiest institutional tools – to engage new visitors and allow and encourage response and discussion. For me, as a researcher exploring connections to, and representations of, community, it is these kinds of programs that employ risky and rich approaches to engagement that are producing the most meaningful results for their visitors. And for this reason the Living Cultures programme is an eloquent reminder that a museum can be more than just a place with things in it.

Sandy O'Sullivan

Australian Research Council Senior Indigenous Research Fellow (Wiradjuri Nation) Batchelor Institute of Indigenous Tertiary Education, Northern Territory, Australia

Below: South African 1994 general election voter education poster. This election marked the end of apartheid. Acquired in 1994.

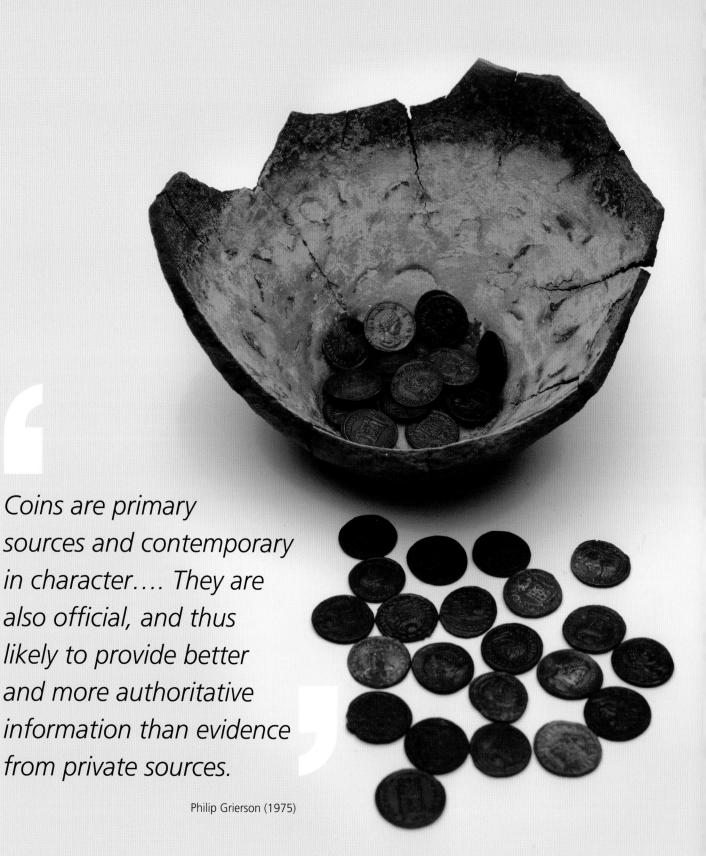

'

*Coins are primary
sources and contemporary
in character.... They are
also official, and thus
likely to provide better
and more authoritative
information than evidence
from private sources.*

Philip Grierson (1975)

'

History and geography in the palm of your hand

Opposite: Pot and coins from the Alderley Edge Hoard.

Below: Silver dekadrachm of Syracuse, c.400 BC.

The holdings of the Manchester Society for the Promotion of Natural History, which provided the foundation for the Manchester Museum, included a small number of coins, the most important of which was a collection of Chinese pieces acquired in the Far East by a local ship's doctor. They are still housed in the individual pill boxes in which they arrived in 1848. It was not until 1894, however, when Reuben Spencer (1830–91) donated his collection of several thousand British and foreign coins, together with commemorative medallions, that the numismatic collection could be regarded as both sizeable and worthy of display. Spencer was chairman of John Rylands and Sons, the largest business organisation in the Manchester area at the time, and a prominent member of the Manchester Museum Committee. His other great gift to the city was the famous library of the same name, which is now part of the University of Manchester.

In the course of the next three decades, the main foundations of the present collection were laid down with the donations of two other long-standing members of the Museum Committee: William Smith Churchill (1826–1914) and William Sharp Ogden (1844–1926). These gifts not only enlarged existing parts of the numismatic collection, but expanded it into other areas, making it comprehensive in scope, if not necessarily in scale. In all, some two-thirds of the coins and medals in the present collection derive from these three generous benefactors. Small donations continued to come in, including a

useful collection of some 400 English copper coins, mostly in mint state, from the first Honorary Keeper of Numismatics, Egmont Steinthal, on leaving Manchester in 1940. The most notable modern gift arrived in 1958, on the sudden death of his successor, Harold Raby, who had been Honorary Keeper of Numismatics since Steinthal's departure. His bequest to the Museum included his magnificent Greek and Roman coins – long recognised as being of national importance – together with English coins and tokens. His own collection had been enriched some 40 years earlier by the purchase of that of Nathan Heywood, a member of the prominent Manchester banking and mayoral family.

With the rise in values of coins and medals in more recent years, donations have become fewer, although the gift in 1991 of an almost complete run of Maundy money from the mid-17th century to the late 1980s, and that of some 4,000 communion tokens bequeathed by a Museum volunteer in 2009, were not only generous, but filled important gaps in the collection.

Occasional purchases have also been made in more recent years to expand the Museum's holdings of Manchester-related medallions, tokens, tickets and passes, an understandably popular topic for the local community, and the one serious weakness in the ancient coin field was addressed in 1997 by the

Above: Silver denarius of Julius Caesar, 44 BC.

False propaganda?

In October 1642, Charles I moved his headquarters to Oxford. This provided him with a great financial boost: he commanded that the colleges give up their gold and silver plate, which was then turned into coinage, of which this silver pound is an example. But the coin is remarkable for other reasons. First, it is the largest silver denomination ever produced in this country, as well as the heaviest; second, the abbreviated Latin inscription on the reverse, which translates as '(I Charles promise to uphold) the protestant religion, the laws of England and the liberty of Parliament', is

a particularly inept attempt at propaganda by the King, whose failure to meet this promise was the cause of the Civil War in the first place.

Above: Unique Isauran 20 nummi of Heraclius, 617–8.

grant-aided purchase of a collection of Byzantine copper coins, amounting to some 1,100 pieces.

Whilst the dedicated Money Gallery showcases the collection, examples are also to be found in the 'Ancient Worlds' displays, and on loan to other institutions. Specimens are frequently used in public programmes, in both the Museum and the wider community, and a selection of Greek, Roman and Byzantine coins feature on relevant postgraduate programmes within the University.

The numismatic holdings of the Manchester Museum now number 55,000 pieces, and are almost universal in scope. In most demand are our Greek, Roman and Byzantine coins, which – at 13,000 specimens – represent almost a quarter of the total collection (and local hoards, particularly Knott Mill and Alderley Edge, add to this number; see text box on p. 131). One highlight is a specialist collection of 1,400 coins of Roman Alexandria, amongst which is one of the few genuine examples of Titiana, wife of the short-lived emperor Pertinax.

Taken together with the colonial holdings, the British coin collection is also large and representative, at 5,800 pieces. The latter ranges from the Celtic period to the 20th century, and, although there is relatively little gold in either series, both contain attractive silver and copper patterns and proofs. Coins from other western countries are also well represented, with a particularly rich collection (6,400 pieces) of German coins, and substantial numbers from Italy, the Low Countries (including issues of the Dutch East Indies), Spain, Russia, France (including colonies) and Switzerland. The overwhelming majority are from the 16th to 19th centuries. Although smaller in size, the Scandinavian collection includes several examples of the famous plate money.

Above: Group of six Roman gold aurei, 1st century AD.

Asian coins are also present in surprisingly large numbers. The dominant collection is the 3,600 coins of the Indian subcontinent, put together by a local antiquarian, Daniel Howorth, a noted authority at a time when few British collectors were interested in the series. The coins were presented to the Museum by a group of his pupils after his death in 1919. They span the whole range of Indian coinage down to the 19th century. Not surprisingly, Chinese coins and charms, ranging in date from the 6th century BC to the early 20th century, are pre-eminent amongst the East Asian holdings. However, there are good numbers of Japanese, Korean and Vietnamese coins, including some extremely rare late 19th-century patterns and proofs.

Medallions were amongst the earliest numismatic objects to enter the collections. Most European and Scandinavian countries are represented, but there is real strength in the English and French material, with more than 500 of each. The medallions are mostly copper, but with a good number of silver examples, and they are overwhelmingly of the 18th and 19th centuries.

The holdings of non-local tokens are almost entirely British, and range from the 17th to the

Right: Pattern gold £5, Queen Victoria, 1839.

20th centuries. They cover the entire 'regular' series, and include large specialist collections of communion tokens and co-operative checks. The 'paranumismatic' section, covering coin and token-like pieces, brings the total numbers to 8,000 items.

In addition, there is a large collection of Manchester-related material containing tokens and advertising pieces, pub and work checks, commemorative and prize medallions, and school and university awards and badges.

Below: Pattern dollar of Ranavalona III of Madagascar, 1862–1917.

Above: Silver presentation 'coin' of Taiping rebellion, China, 1850–64.

63

Below: Gilt medallion on the execution of Louis XVI and Marie Antionette, France.

Last but not least, the Museum possesses an unexpected treasure: a large part of the medallic archive of Edward Carter Preston (1885–1965), the 20th century's leading war medal artist. His career encompassed five decades of official work for the Royal Mint – from the Next-of-Kin plaque of the First World War to the Korean War Medal of the 1950s – as well as numerous private medallic commissions. The archive contains sketches and finished drawings, moulds and plasters, and the artist's own examples of his finished medals.

A beautiful Chinese coin

The inscription on this Chinese coin reads *Chongning tongbao* ('circulating treasure in the reign of Chongning'). It was issued between 1102 and 1106, under the Emperor Huizong. This piece is particularly interesting for the style of its inscription. Calligraphy has always been considered as the highest form of art in China, exceeding even painting and sculpture. The aesthetic value of the coin is expressed by calligraphic inscription, rather than images (there were no Chinese coins with a portrait of an Emperor until the early 20th century). Emperor Huizong was known for his proficiency in art and literature, and he himself wrote out the original inscription for the *Chongning tongbao* coin, using a style of calligraphy created by himself, later known as 'Slender Gold'. The coin has been greatly admired ever since.

"*I had no idea that Manchester could boast such a rich and varied coin collection!*"

Visitor to Money Gallery

Numismatics

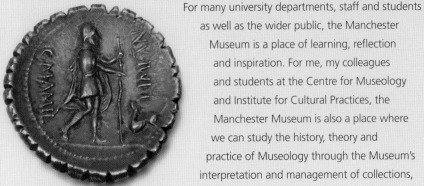

For many university departments, staff and students as well as the wider public, the Manchester Museum is a place of learning, reflection and inspiration. For me, my colleagues and students at the Centre for Museology and Institute for Cultural Practices, the Manchester Museum is also a place where we can study the history, theory and practice of Museology through the Museum's interpretation and management of collections, development of exhibitions and community engagement activities. Indeed, the Centre for Museology, Institute for Cultural Practices and the Manchester Museum have an established and ever-developing relationship that includes a variety of collaborations, in teaching, professional development and research. The Museum is an experienced provider of work placements for students not only in our MAs in 'Art Gallery and Museum Studies' and 'Arts Management, Policy and Practice', but in programmes across the University. These placements allow students to gain first-hand experience of various aspects of the Museum operation, under the close supervision of experienced Museum staff, and develop a better understanding of the issues and challenges in caring for collections and developing rewarding experiences for visitors. Also, having access to the behind-the-scenes processes of curating collections and preparing exhibitions at the Manchester Museum offers students an invaluable opportunity to link theory and practice. Manchester Museum colleagues contribute further to this bridging of theory and practice in university teaching through visiting lectures, seminars and workshops, and supporting student projects and dissertations. This active engagement of

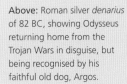

Above: Roman silver *denarius* of 82 BC, showing Odysseus returning home from the Trojan Wars in disguise, but being recognised by his faithful old dog, Argos.

the Manchester Museum with the training of future arts and Museum professionals is an invaluable offer that both students and staff appreciate greatly. For me personally, the Manchester Museum is an exemplary university museum that aims to push boundaries in exhibition making, challenge preconceptions in understanding objects and collections, be open to new visitor-focused ideas, reflect critically on its own practice and share generously all this with University teachers and students and the wider audience.

Kostas Arvanitis
Lecturer in Museology, University of Manchester

> I find in Geology a never failing interest, as it has been remarked, it creates the same grand ideas respecting this world, which Astronomy does for the universe.

Charles Darwin

The story of Earth and early life

05

Opposite: Cast of *Tyrannosaurus rex*, originally found in South Dakota, USA.

Below right: The footprint of a 240-million-year-old reptile called *Chirotherium*, from Cheshire.

Geology uses rocks, fossils and minerals to help us understand the planet and life on Earth. The Manchester Museum has about 100,000 fossils and 40,000 rocks and minerals in the collection. It is one of the largest and most important geology collections in Britain.

Enthusiastic members of the Manchester Geological Society started collecting rocks, fossils and minerals in 1838, and the original Manchester Museum on Peter Street (see figure on p. 11) included some spectacular geology. Some of the highlights were a large Ichthyosaur (on display in the Museum today), a hexagonal basalt pillar from the Giant's Causeway, and models of famous diamonds.

As we have seen earlier, William Boyd Dawkins (1837–1929) was probably the most influential person in the early life of the Manchester Museum. He was appointed the first curator at the Manchester Museum in 1869, and made sure geology was at the heart of the new University museum when it opened to the public in 1890. He was the first person to organise the eclectic science collections, and his collecting, research and teaching established the Manchester Museum as a national player. He spent much of his career researching cave fossils and early human evolution. His work centred on Windy Knoll, near Castleton and Creswell Crags. Boyd Dawkins' publication *Cave Hunting* was the first time the growing mass of material, unearthed in numerous sites in Europe, had been covered in a single volume.

The Fossils

Fossils are evidence of life on Earth, often millions of years old. The bones, shells and other traces of life give us clues to the plants and animals that lived in

Percy the Plesiosaur

A spectacular plesiosaur fossil was discovered in 1960, by students from the University of Manchester while on a field trip led by Dr Fred Broadhurst. The students were studying the geology of the Yorkshire coast at Robin Hood's Bay, North Yorkshire, when they spotted the tip of something interesting projecting from the rocky shore. After a little more excavation, the head, neck and one paddle-shaped arm of a plesiosaur were revealed. The fossil was at an angle to the surface, which meant that the body and tail were much deeper than the head. Fred quickly realised that the rest was too deep, and that they would have to return to complete the excavation. He led the group of six research students who worked for two days in appalling weather conditions with driving sleet and hail. The plesiosaur was recorded in detail before being carefully removed in three large blocks. With incredible effort, the blocks were carried over the boulders on the beach. They were then dragged up the cliffs on a section of ladder found on the beach. Everyone was roped in to

help, forming a human 'husky dog' team. The fossil was nicknamed Percy. Back at the University, the painstaking process of extracting the fossil from the rock began. The fossil turned out to be one of the most complete plesiosaurs ever discovered. Detailed research shows that this fossil is a 180-million-year-old new species, classified as *Hauffiosaurus tomistomimus*. Scientists from around the world continue to study this unique specimen.

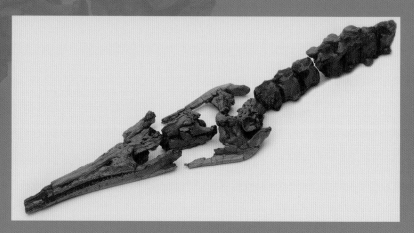

Below: Skull of Percy the Plesiosaur.

the past. The Manchester Museum has always been well placed to collect the best of the fossils from the Carboniferous Limestone reefs of Derbyshire, spectacular reptile footprints from the Triassic deserts of Cheshire and plant and other fossils from the coal mines of the north-west often made their way to the Museum. The Manchester Museum's fossils have helped form the foundations of geology, for example through the work of W.C. Williamson (1826–95), a famous palaeobotanist, who used the Museum's fossil plants to help transform our understanding of the Jurassic period and develop the science of palaeobotany.

S.S. Buckman (1860–1929), a famous geologist, found that ammonite fossils look different depending on how old the rocks are. He showed that these patterns are the same wherever they are found, and used ammonites to tell the age of rocks precisely. This was the first time fossils had been used in this way, and established one of the principles of geology. Most of his fossils are now in the Museum collection.

One of the most important collections at the Museum is from Creswell Crags near Chesterfield, Derbyshire. The collection charts the changes in climate during the last Ice Age, when humans

Above: Hyena skull from Mother Grundy's Parlour, Creswell Crags, about 20,000 years old.

Below right: A. Leslie Armstrong and Mr Garfitt, excavating Mother Grundy's Parlour, Creswell Crags, early 1920s.

first lived in Britain. Animals such as hyena, hippopotamus and mammoth moved in and out of Britain following their food. The collection has helped transform our understanding of science. The fossils from Creswell Crags give a rare glimpse into what was happening at the extreme northerly edge of life in the last Ice Age, and a window into the world of the first people to live in Britain.

As noted earlier, A. Leslie Armstrong (1879–1958) conducted some of the most comprehensive excavations at Creswell Crags, donating much of his collection to the Manchester Museum. Armstrong's scientific approach, excavating 6–8-inch layers and sieving the sediment so that small remains were recovered, and his meticulous recording of the location of the finds, laid the foundations for the scientific study of Creswell Crags, which still continues today.

Other spectacular fossils at the Museum include: some of the earliest life on Earth from Ediacara, Australia, a cast of the most complete *Tyrannosaurus rex* ever discovered (see image on p. 66), large marine reptiles and a tree fossil. The Museum has an encyclopaedic collection of 300-million-year-old fossil plants from the local coal-bearing rocks, stunning fossils from the Solnhofen Limestone where *Archaeopteryx* was discovered, and a substantial collection of trilobites and ammonites.

Left: A selection of gems and semi-precious stones from the mineral collection.

Below: Marie Stopes using a microscope to study fossil plants.

The Manchester Museum geology collection not only includes important specimens, but also helps chart the social history of some of the pioneers of the 20th century. Marie Stopes (1880–1958) is best known as a social reformer, but before this she was a geologist in Manchester. In 1904, she was the first woman to be appointed to the scientific staff at the University of Manchester, where she undertook research into coal fossils and Jurassic plants, and her signature is recorded on many of the fossils in the Museum's collection. Her research formed one of the foundations of modern coal geology. She met Robert Falcon Scott while at Manchester, where she almost certainly showed him examples of *Glossopteris* fossil plants in the collection. Scott went on to collect

The finest specimen ever discovered

The tree fossil (called Stigmaria ficoides) is one of the most spectacular fossil plants in the world. It was discovered on 8 July 1886, at Clayton near Bradford, Yorkshire. At the time it was described as 'The finest specimen ever discovered'. The specimen was purchased for the Museum by W.C. Williamson. An account by a third party of Williamson's trip to look at the newly discovered fossil is recorded in his memoir *Reminiscences of a Yorkshire naturalist*: 'On the morning we had arranged to see the Clayton tree, rain poured in torrents, and I tried in vain to persuade Dr Williamson to postpone his journey.' When he reached the quarry not a living soul was near, only the grey sky above, grey Yorkshire hills around, and the storm raging, when the old geologist met face to face the thing he had hoped so long to see. As he stood and gazed at the calm big tree spreading its roots in every direction, and apparently as full of life as it had ever been, the quarry master appeared, looking astonished, and said, 'Not Professor Williamson!' 'Certainly.' 'And from Manchester this morning,' said the shivering owner. 'Yes, and why not?' 'Well, sir,' answered he, 'to my thinking, you and the tree are a pair, for teaching us lessons.' We don't have a record of how the fossil was transported to the Museum, but it was most likely broken into sections and transported over the hills and moors by horse and cart. This fossil would have been closely related to modern mosses, but would have reached around 30 metres high when it fruited.

Right: The fossil tree still in the quarry, as it was found in 1886,

fossils of this type on his fateful polar expedition in 1912. Scott's fossils later became a key piece of evidence for reconstructing the ancient super-continent called Gondwanaland. On a research trip to Japan, Marie discovered the earliest recorded evidence of flowering plants. Beautiful fossil leaves from one of her other collecting trips form part of the Museum's collection.

Professor Friedrich Paneth (1887–1958) was a notable chemist and an avid amber collector. Born in Vienna, Paneth was a pioneer in the new field of radiochemistry, working at various universities around Europe and in the USA. In 1929, he became Professor of Chemistry at Königsberg, a world-famous amber site. In 1933, the Nazis came to power and the future for the Jews in Königsberg looked bleak. Paneth was on a lecture tour in Britain at the time and stayed on. He later joined the staff of Imperial College London, and in 1953 became director of the Max Planck Institute for Chemistry at Mainz, Germany, where he remained for the rest of his life. Paneth's stunning amber

collection was put together while he lived in Königsberg, and some 40 specimens came to the Museum after his death. The 40-million-year-old Baltic amber includes 21 specimens containing insects such as ants, spiders and flies.

THE MINERALS

Minerals are naturally occurring chemical substances. They form the building blocks of rocks in the same way ingredients are mixed and baked to make a cake. The Manchester Museum's stunning collection of 20,000 minerals gives a taste of the seemingly endless diversity of colour, shape and form found in nature. Rare metal ores and crystals, which grow in just a few special places, sit alongside valuable gemstones.

The collection is particularly rich in minerals from Britain and Ireland, with good specimens from Alderley Edge (see text box on p. 131), Cheshire, Cumbria and western Scotland. The collection includes internationally important specimens collected by H.F. Harwood from around the

Below: Ant preserved in 40-million-year-old Baltic amber.

Left: Calcite from Egremont, Cumbria.

> "The Museum is so good that I would explode if I saw any more. The T. rex is especially good because it's towering above you and it looks so real."
>
> Visitor to the Fossils Gallery

world. The Museum cares for the first specimen ever seen of a new copper mineral called Redgillite. It was discovered in 1989, by Peter Braithwaite, David Green and Jean Spence in Silver Gill mine in Cumbria, and described as a new mineral to science in 2005.

THE ROCKS

Rocks are the foundation of planet Earth. They form in mountains, rivers, volcanoes and the sea. The mix of minerals can tell us about where they formed and how they ended up where they are today. The rock collection gives an insight into the monumental processes that continue to shape our changing planet.

Specimens of the oldest rocks in the UK show the immense heat and pressure that have distorted them over millions of years, while fragile stalactites chart the changing climate of the last Ice Age. The collection includes delicate volcanic foam from the mouth of a Hawaiian volcano, and Icelandic ash from the Eyjafjallajökull eruption of 2010.

Above: The world's first specimen of Redgillite, found in 1989.

Right: Volcanic foam from Hawaii.

A fireball over Cheshire

At 8:45pm on 13 October 1914, a fireball was seen over Lancashire and Cheshire; then 'a thunder-like explosion' was heard. Local people feared it was a German attack. People from as far away as Liverpool and Halifax had witnessed the event. The morning after, a farm worker noticed a mound running across a field at Appley Bridge, near Wigan. At the end of the mound, in a 45cm hole, was a 15kg meteorite. The meteorite was first handed over to the police, who then gave it to the Godlee Observatory, now part of the University of Manchester. Analysis of the crater and the sightings showed that it travelled at a very low angle. It was first sighted near Stoke before travelling the 49 miles to Appley Bridge at more than 8 miles per second. The Appley Bridge meteorite belongs to a group called the stony meteorites. A plaster cast was made of the meteorite before it was sliced up for analysis.

> *"Very different to other museums. I loved it!"*
>
> Visitor to the Fossils Gallery

Below: Cast of the Appley Bridge meteorite, alongside a piece of the original.

Objects in the collection give a key insight into the social history of Manchester and its geologists. Building stones chart the development of the city and samples of rock from under the English Channel record an aborted attempt at building the Channel Tunnel in 1882 (see also the text and photo on p. 126). The Manchester Museum geology collection has played a key role in inspiring and amazing visitors, researchers and students alike. It gives us a unique window onto the life and processes that have shaped the Earth over the last 4.5 billion years. The collection continues to help transform our understanding of science and the people who shaped society.

Earth Sciences

The Palaeontology collection at the Manchester Museum provides comprehensive fossil evidence of the evolution of life on Earth. The remarkable adaptations acquired by species through time are echoed in the endless forms that are found in the fossil record. From single-celled organisms to the evolution of the first multicellular animals, the march of life endures on our planet today. Fossils housed in museums such as this provide crucial evidence for the natural selective processes that have impacted upon the evolution of life. As you walk from case to case in the Fossils Gallery, you time-travel to past worlds when the planet was a very different place.

The image of our planet that we all recognise from space today would have been radically different in deep time. The interconnected tectonic plates that form the surface of Earth have had a restless history. The global ballet of plates affected landmasses, oceans and seas, slowly shifting relative positions through geological time, roughly at the same speed at which your toenails grow! Our dynamic Earth has indirectly driven the evolution of life, steering change in global climates and subsequent environments. As the position of landmasses 'drifted' from one climatic regime to another, the fauna and flora had to migrate, adapt or shuffle into extinction. Today we talk of environmental disaster due to global warming, as we drive our climate toward a 'greenhouse' planet. Our current 'disaster' was the past reality for dinosaurs who prospered in a 'greenhouse' planet between 230–65 million years ago. Polar dinosaurs once wandered the temperate forests of Antarctica – a far cry from the frozen wastelands we see at the poles today. The past environments that left such an indelible mark in the sands of time can help researchers on my team understand the future of our green planet. The Manchester Museum fossils provide the time capsule of life that fuels this research.

Phillip Lars Manning
Senior Lecturer, Earth, Atmospheric and Environmental Sciences, University of Manchester

Until science is mixed with emotion and appeals to the heart and imagination, it is like dead organic matter.

John Burroughs (1889)

A is for Aardvark, Z is for Zebra

Opposite: View of the Zoology store.

Below: Skull of 'Old Billy'. He lived near Manchester during 1760–1822.

Below right: Oil painting of 'Old Billy' by Charles Towne, painted shortly before the horse died.

The Museum has several galleries of mounted animals that follow the visitor around with their glass eyes, but there is much more to zoology than that. Preserved animals have strong popular appeal and, most importantly, they help us to understand the living world. The Museum's zoology collections contain the preserved remains of dead animals and parts of dead animals, collected during four centuries.

They are certainly among the finest in the UK, in terms of numbers of specimens and species, and are a crucial element of the present Museum collection.

Animals were a particular focus of 19th-century collectors and the private members of the Manchester Society for the Promotion of Natural History (1821–67) gathered their collections together in the Society's museum in the city centre. Among

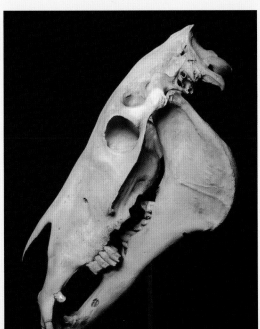

the wonderful curios in the entrance hall of the old museum were a narwhal's tusk, a mounted giraffe and elephant, and a cast of the head of the extinct dodo. A pair of mounted dogs of an extinct local breed, the Lyme Hall Mastiff, stood on pedestals on either side of the main staircase. Of particular interest was the skull of 'Old Billy', a horse which was, and still is, reckoned to be the longest-lived horse, at 62 years of age. Also dating from the Society's early collections is the mounted skin of a cow of the British White breed, from the now-extinct herd at Gisburne Park in Lancashire. This particular cow died in 1837, and the mounted skin is still in existence (with a rather spooky blue glass eye). 'Mr Potter's Cow' is among the oldest mounted specimens in the present museum. It is in remarkably good condition, perhaps because it was used to demonstrate cleaning techniques to the public in what was known as 'the cow-washing ceremony'.

The Society's collections were more than just a series of curios: among them was one of the shell collections of the famous William Swainson, purchased for a fortune (£650) in 1825. The bird

Above: Skeleton of a young sperm whale found dying on sea ice in Massachusetts in 1896.

Below: Study skin of a warbler finch (*Certhidea olivacea*) collected by Charles Darwin on the Galapagos Islands in 1835 during his famous voyage on HMS *Beagle*.

Darwin's Finch

The Museum collections contain some specimens that have been very influential in our understanding of the world. Among these is a tiny bird that looks a bit like a wren, greenish with a thin beak. Except this isn't a wren, it is a finch, and it comes from the Galapagos Islands. This specimen was collected by Charles Darwin on the islands in 1835, on the famous voyage of HMS *Beagle*. Darwin was struck by the differences between the mockingbirds he saw on the different islands, but it wasn't until he returned to England that the ornithologist John Gould told him that the small birds he had collected were all members of one particular group of birds, although their beaks looked so different. Writing in the 'Journal of Researches' (better known as 'The Voyage of the Beagle'), Darwin wrote how 'one might really fancy that from an original paucity of birds in this archipelago, one species had been taken and modified for different ends'. These specimens were very influential in how Darwin developed his ideas on evolution by natural selection, which were presented in *On the Origin of Species* in 1859, arguably the most important biology book of all time.

> **"***When I get home I am going to hang out my bird feeder.***"**
>
> Museum visitor

collection was described as 'the first in the provinces of Britain if not in Europe' in 1839. The taxidermist caused a stir by inserting glass eyes, which were expensive, in only the viewable sides of specimens, in order to save money. The Museum still has many of these one-eyed birds. Most of the animals on display today date from that early period, perhaps excusing the rather tired expressions on their faces. Unfortunately the history of many specimens is not well understood.

The transfer of the collections to their present location during 1868–73 caused great public amusement and was likened to a travelling circus, with the mounted animals carried through the streets of Manchester on carts. Zoology featured heavily in the present museum when it first opened in 1891, with galleries dedicated to mammals, birds and invertebrates. One significant early addition was that of the skeleton of a young sperm whale, which had washed ashore on the ice in New Bedford (Massachusetts) in 1896. The skeleton was bought for £60 and shipped to the Manchester docks in three

huge crates. A photograph still exists of the local taxidermist hanging the skeleton from the roof of the galleries. It took him three weeks to put the skeleton together, in 1898. The skeleton has hung there ever since (see also text box on pp. 116–7).

The Museum's collections grew very rapidly after opening to the public, and included examples of most animal groups. University lecturers formed collections and studied specimens that were often passed on to the Museum. Sydney Hickson (1859–1940), Professor of Zoology, was an expert on corals and had explored Celebes (now Sulawesi) in the Indo-Pacific. Many of his specimens are still in the Museum, including some that were the basis of new species he described for the first time (type specimens). Grafton Elliot Smith (1871–1937), Professor of Anatomy, was one of those involved in the initial investigations of Piltdown Man, the most important scientific forgery in history. This may explain why the Museum has so much material from Piltdown, including many casts and some gravel from the site. Museum staff also undertook their

Right: Type specimen of a coral named *Stylaster tiliatus* (now *Stenohelia tiliata*) by Sydney Hickson and Helen England in 1905. Collected on the 'Siboga' expedition to Indonesia (1899–1900).

Far right: Parasitic worms (*Acanthocephalans*) attached to the intestine of a false killer whale, history unknown but dating from the early 20th century.

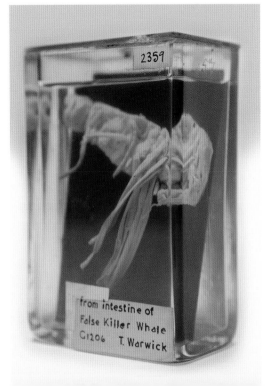

The Museum has benefited greatly as a result of transfers and exchanges with other museums around the world, notably 1,400 bird skins (from the most famous collectors) and large numbers of duplicates from the 'Challenger' expedition received from the British Museum (Natural History) in 1895 and 1900 respectively. Other specimens have included a polar bear received as a flat skin from a museum in Dundee in 1907; this had been acquired from a whaling ship that had sailed to Arctic America.

Apart from University and Museum staff, the early Museum received many collections from private naturalists, including wealthy Manchester industrialists. One of these was James Cosmo Melvill (1845–1929), who worked as a cotton merchant and gathered enormous collections of plants and shells from around the world. He worked with Robert Standen (1854–1925), who was on the Museum staff, to describe new species of mollusc from the collections he purchased and received. Many of their type specimens are still in the Museum

Above: Mounted polar bear, taken as a flat skin from Arctic America to Dundee by a whaling ship around 1905.

own scientific investigations. Two were involved in the 'Challenger' expedition (1872–6) investigations: William Hoyle (1855–1926) was the first Keeper of the Museum and studied the octopus and squid from the expedition, naming many new species. Frederick Pearcey (1855–1927), had actually been on the 'Challenger' expedition; he worked in the Museum as an assistant keeper.

Left: *Conus clytospira*, described as a new species by Cosmo Melvill and Robert Standen in 1899. This specimen was found attached to a submarine telegraph cable in the Persian Gulf and still has some tar from the cable on its surface.

Below: Microscope slide showing single-celled marine animals called Foraminifera arranged by species. These were collected during the 'Challenger' expedition of 1872–6 and prepared by Frederick Pearcey.

Below right: Mounted giant tortoise, taken alive from the Galapagos Islands in 1897–8. The tortoise lived at Tring Park in Hertfordshire for several years before being given, dead, to the Museum in 1904.

collection and are frequently consulted by experts. The Museum received a handful of specimens from Walter Rothschild, an obsessive and fabulously wealthy collector from the famous banking family. Among these was the body of a giant tortoise that had been taken alive from the Galapagos Islands in 1898 at a time when Rothschild was concerned that humans were eating the tortoises out of existence.

Arthur Waters (1846–1929) was a local private zoologist; he used his time to study a particular group of small colonial marine animals called Bryozoa, which look like slightly crusty seaweed. Waters was awarded the Challenger Medal for his investigation of the Bryozoa collected during the 'Challenger' expedition. His collection of tens of thousands of Bryozoa is one of the Museum's most scientifically important groups, as it contains around 400 type specimens. Apart from Waters' material, the Museum also contains the Bryozoa collection formed by Eliza Jelly (1829–1914) who, as a woman, was unusual among bryozoologists of the time. In addition, the Museum contains important collections of microscope slides of single-celled marine animals. These were popular subjects for

naturalists at the turn of the 20th century, when this was a popular hobby, and similar collections are found in other parts of the Museum.

The pace of collecting slowed through the 20th century, and most material was received from private collectors or their descendents as collecting became unfashionable. Lord Maurice Egerton (1874–1958) was a keen big-game hunter. 'Lord Egerton's Antelopes' are particularly fine examples of taxidermy and were prepared by the famous firm of Rowland Ward; these were donated to the Museum from the 1920s onwards. Another particularly notable acquisition from this time was the skeleton of 'Maharajah', a famous elephant that was sold to Belle Vue Zoo by an Edinburgh circus in 1872 and walked with his keeper all the way to Manchester. On his death, his skeleton was purchased from the zoo.

More recently, the Museum acquired the collections of snails belonging to Arthur Cain

(1921–99), Professor of Zoology in the University of Manchester, and Arthur Stelfox (1883–1972). Cain studied the genetics of banding in snails, while Stelfox selectively bred snails for a period of 60 years, producing extraordinary lengthened specimens. The Museum's bird collection, always a strong point, continued to be a focus for collecting during the period when Dr Mike Hounsome was Keeper of Zoology, and bird skins and skeletons continue to be added to the collection. Other major additions have come as a result of the transfer of teaching collections from elsewhere in the University, including large collections of animal bones and skeletons.

Today, the collections are among the top five in the UK. They are much more than a 'dead zoo': in an age of habitat loss and extinction they are an archive of the natural diversity that has existed, and an inspiration to people to preserve the diversity that remains.

Above: Skeleton of 'Maharajah', an Asian elephant that was famous as 'the elephant who walked to Manchester' from Edinburgh in 1872 before living at Belle Vue Zoo.

Above left: Garden snails studied by Arthur Stelfox. For 60 years he bred snails to have increasingly pointed shell shapes.

Henry Dresser

Museums are filled with objects, but who collected them? Why did they do it? These are not always easy questions to answer, but we do know a great deal about some collectors and their 'ruling passions'. Henry Eeles Dresser (1838–1915) was a leading British ornithologist from the 1850s until his death. His letters and publications are scattered around in different archives and museums, but with a bit of detective work these can give an insight into his personality, activities and motivations. Dresser had an unusual education in northern Europe to prepare him for a life in the timber business. Throughout his career he travelled very widely on business and was in Texas during the American civil war. Dresser was completely obsessed with collecting birds and eggs, and could stuff birds before the age of 14. He began collecting birds and eggs systematically in order to write about them and received specimens from the most famous collectors. Dresser wrote books and articles about birds in the evenings after work in the City in London, mostly based on his own specimens. The Museum acquired his bird skin collection in 1899 and his egg collection in 1910. He is particularly notable as he was involved in drawing up the first bird conservation laws in Britain and had a leading role in several scientific societies.

Above: Henry Dresser, at the age of about 60.

Zoology

As a biologist who is interested in how plants and animals live, I think the Manchester Museum is a vitally important part of the University. I have often sent students to the geology and natural history galleries to see the organisms I have been teaching them about, and to learn first hand about the evolution of life. The curatorial staff help run our field courses, supervise research projects for final-year students, and the collections and expertise they hold are vital for anyone needing to identify organisms. But even more important than its academic relationship to the University is its educational role for the city as a whole. Helping to run Big Saturdays, displaying stick insects and ferns, I have always been struck by the sheer enjoyment contact with living plants and animals gives to both children and their parents. This is just one example of the benefits of having such a wide collection of real objects, which are far more magical and inspiring than the virtual world of computers. Personally I also love coming to the Museum. For a start there is the beautiful Waterhouse building itself, which takes me back to my childhood visits to the Natural History Museum. Then there are the wonderful exhibits – my favourites are the huge club moss tree in the geology gallery, the wonderful archery collection, and of course the marvellous vivarium. Seeing the happiness of visitors both young and old it is clear to me that the Museum is a vital beacon of civilisation and education. A visit always raises my spirits and long may it continue to delight us all.

Roland Ennos

Reader in Ecology, University of Manchester

Without [collections], there could be no more Entomology than there could be science without books.

John Lubbock (1856)

A collection of inordinate number and diversity

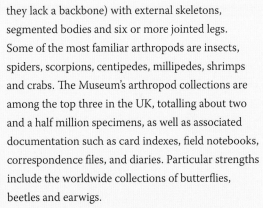

07

Opposite: *Gloriana ornata*, a spectacular noctuid moth from India that resembles dried leaves when at rest, from the C.H. Schill World Lepidoptera collection.

Below: View of an insect collection area in the Manchester Museum.

Of the hidden treasures at the Manchester Museum, the collection of arthropods deposited in the Entomology Department is exceptionally important both in terms of number and diversity. This is hardly surprising, as more than three out of four of all animals on Earth are arthropods. These are invertebrate animals (meaning they lack a backbone) with external skeletons, segmented bodies and six or more jointed legs. Some of the most familiar arthropods are insects, spiders, scorpions, centipedes, millipedes, shrimps and crabs. The Museum's arthropod collections are among the top three in the UK, totalling about two and a half million specimens, as well as associated documentation such as card indexes, field notebooks, correspondence files, and diaries. Particular strengths include the worldwide collections of butterflies, beetles and earwigs.

One of the first questions that may occur to a visitor to the Museum's Entomology Department is: what is the use of having all these specimens? The collections are so large that their full diversity is impossible to display. A quick answer is that all these specimens constitute an essential archive of research. Thousands of specimens retained in the Department are examples of organisms collected in the course of taxonomic or biodiversity research. They are called 'voucher specimens' and are physical proof that species have been recorded from the studied site

Right: The giant spider crab (*Macrocheira kaempferi*), the largest living arthropod from the collection of marine Crustacea (c.540 species) deposited in the Manchester Museum. This crab occurs on the sea bed off Japan at depths of 200–300m. Males of these crabs weigh up to 20kg, and their leg span can reach 4m.

and identified accurately. Every specimen represents an essential and irreplaceable source of information for research, aiming to answer three fundamental questions: *what* is the organism under study, *where* is it found in nature, and *why* is it found there? Without such reference collections, acting as a kind of 'biological library', most taxonomic, biodiversity or conservation research cannot be conducted.

The origin of the Manchester Museum's arthropod collections dates back to the foundation of the Museum by the Manchester Society for the Promotion of Natural History in 1821 (see p. 12). The oldest insect specimens in the

Museum are the beetles collected by William Kirby (1759–1850), the founder of English entomology, and described by Thomas Marsham (–1819) in his *Entomologica Britannica* in 1802. The original arrangement and nucleus of the Museum's entomological collections was assembled by John R. Hardy (1844–1921), who was appointed as a 'Senior Assistant Keeper and

Below: The elephant beetle (*Megasoma elephas*), one of the largest beetles on Earth, known from the lowland rainforests of Central and South America. Males can reach the length of 120mm and their weight can exceed 50–70g.

Left: The pill-beetle, (*Cistela maritima*), described in 1802, the oldest insect specimen at the Manchester Museum.

The Manchester Moth

The most famous specimen in the Entomology collection is the celebrated Manchester Moth (*Euclemensia woodiella*). It is a tiny, delicate moth, with a wingspan of less than one centimetre. Only three specimens of this moth are available today: in the Melbourne Museum (Australia), in the Natural History Museum (London), and in the Manchester Museum. The Manchester Museum's specimen is badly damaged, with most of its legs, right antenna and half of the abdomen missing, and with the right forewing torn apart. Here we present an accurate reconstruction of the moth. The Manchester Moth remains an unsolved scientific conundrum. Originally, in June 1829, a series of 50/60 specimens was collected by the amateur collector Robert Cribb from Kearsall Moor (Salford, Greater Manchester). He gave one specimen to John Curtis (1791–1862), an eminent authority on insects, who described the moth as a new species in 1830. Two specimens of the moth were also given to the local collector S. Carter. Unfortunately, the storage box containing the rest of specimens of the original series was destroyed by Cribb's landlady in revenge for rent arrears. Since then, nobody else has been able to collect any further specimens, and the moth has not been seen alive. It is believed that this species does not occur outside Britain and is now most likely extinct.

Below: A unit-tray of Morpho butterflies from the C.H. Schill World Lepidoptera collection.

Above: A reconstruction of the Manchester Moth.

Entomology Curator' in January 1908. He also obtained a great deal of exotic material, of which the C.H. Schill collection of butterflies and moths was particularly important. This worldwide collection is a real treasure of the Museum. It includes some 40,000 specimens of over 8,000 species from all families of butterflies, larger moths and tiny moths commonly known as micro-Lepidoptera (i.e., having a wingspan of less than one centimetre). The collection contains some currently threatened or extinct species, for instance the Sloane's Urania, one of the most spectacular day-flying moth species that was endemic to the island of Jamaica. The moth was last reported in 1894 or 1895, and most probably disappeared due to habitat loss when Jamaica's lowland rainforests were cleared and converted to agricultural land.

The Manchester Museum holds a comprehensive collection of British insects totalling some 720,000 specimens of 13,845 species, and overall accounting for about 60% of all the insect species recorded in the UK. It is the finest collection of British insects in the North-West, which is regularly consulted by local entomologists and university students. The person primarily responsible for building it up was Harry Britten (1870–1954), a self-educated ex-railwayman without a formal academic background, who became recognized as one of the greatest British entomologists in the 20th century. During his keepership (1919–38), Britten paid particular attention to the so-called 'critical groups in entomology' (parasitic wasps, true flies, bristletails, lice, and some others) which were lacking at the Museum and were largely ignored at his time by other entomologists. His abilities as a field naturalist and his manipulative skills in dissecting and mounting insects were legendary. He devised an original method of 'side mounting' of specimens,

> **"** I really enjoyed looking at the spiders … the thing that I loved most was drawing on the hairy detail. **"**
>
> Raquel (aged 9)

Above: The Sloane's Urania (*Urania sloanus*), an extinct species of which only three specimens are deposited in the Manchester Museum.

Left: Harry Britten, the former Keeper of Entomology of the Manchester Museum, at the time of his presidency of the Manchester Entomological Society (1922–3).

each with a neat handwritten label, so that many thousands of the specimens mounted by him are easily recognizable in the collection.

In 1919, Britten acquired Joseph Sidebotham's collection of butterflies and moths (1,867 species), a good example of the Victorian private entomological collection. Sidebotham (1824–85) was a calico printer and JP. His interests ranged from botany and entomology through astronomy and photography. He also collected diatoms (a group of single-celled or colonial algae having cell walls composed of silica, see photo on p. 129) and was one of the founders of the Manchester Field Naturalists' Society. All his specimens are superbly mounted, reliably identified and are in perfect condition. However, only a few of them contain locality labels. It is known nevertheless that the majority of specimens in the Sidebotham collection were collected in Britain in the late 19th century, but some might have originated from France. Since that time several species have already become extinct in the UK, for instance the Large Copper butterfly and the Large Blue.

Another important Museum collection acquired by Britten is the world collection of Swallowtail

Right: A specimen of the cranefly (*Tipula vernalis*) mounted and labelled by H. Britten.

Below: Four colour morphs of the Scarlet Tiger (*Callimorpha dominula*), a scarce British species represented by 20 specimens in the collection of J. Sidebotham.

butterflies, which was received by bequest of David Longsdon (–1937) in 1937–8. It is not only a valuable collection from a scientific point of view, but also has considerable monetary value. The collection contains more than 9,200 specimens representing practically all known species of Swallowtail butterflies. It is nicely organized and rich in data (labels are dated from 1890 to 1936) and contains lots of rarities, such as a series of six specimens of the Hahnel's Amazonian Swallowtail, known from only a few localities of central Brazil.

By far, the largest and most scientifically important are the Museum's collections of beetles, the largest group of animals in the world (in terms of numbers of described species), representing one fifth of all known living organisms. Our beetle collections represent the legacy of one of England's greatest entomologists, Walter Douglas Hincks (1906–61), who began as the Museum's

Assistant Keeper in Entomology in 1947. Hincks wanted to make the Entomology Department the finest reference and study centre in the North and thus his keepership (1947–61) saw massive improvements to the collections. With his friend John Dibb (1906–73), who was an insurance surveyor by profession and an entomologist by devotion, he built up very extensive collections of foreign

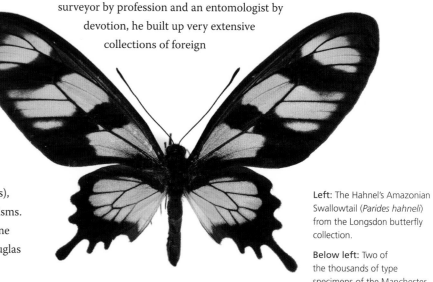

Left: The Hahnel's Amazonian Swallowtail (*Parides hahneli*) from the Longsdon butterfly collection.

Below left: Two of the thousands of type specimens of the Manchester Museum's collection of tortoise beetles (Cassidinae), *Meroscalsis dohertyi* (left) and *Lorentzocassis papuana* (right).

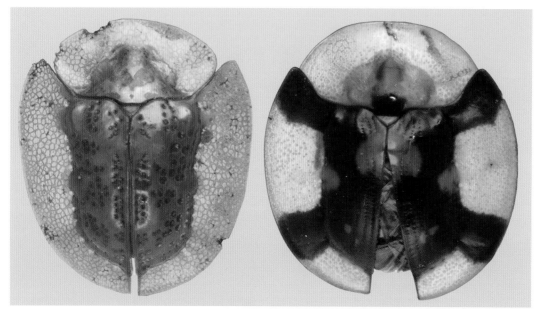

Dodo of the earwigs

The Entomology Department retains specimens of a number of extremely rare or already extinct insects. One of them is the magnificent Giant Earwig (*Labidura herculeana*), of which the Museum holds only two specimens, a male and a female. The giant earwig is the world's largest earwig, and derives from the small volcanic island of St Helena in the South Atlantic. Its body length ranges from 36 to 54 millimetres. The largest known specimen is a male of about 78mm long. The creature is also known as the 'Dodo of the earwigs', since it was endemic to a small island and is likely to have become extinct. Fundamental reasons for its disappearance seem to have been the clearing of the Gumwood forest where the species occurred and its predation by introduced animals, particularly by the large centipede (*Scolopendra morsitans*) and mice. Since 1967, when the earwig was still reasonably common, it has not been seen alive, though three unsuccessful expeditions have been organized and sponsored by the London Zoo in order to find and rescue it. However, the earwig has entered into the folklore of St Helena, and many people believe that it is still living out there somewhere.

beetles from all over the world. These collections came to the Museum at varying times through Hincks. One of the most important acquisitions he made was the worldwide collection of tortoise-beetles (Cassidinae) of the late Franz Spaeth (1863–1946), the main world authority on the group at that time. The collection was built up by Spaeth for nearly half a century and contained more than 20,000 beetles, including some 3,000 type specimens. It was the finest private collection of the group, exceeding in scientific value those of all European museums. The collection was purchased by the Museum in 1950 through the financial assistance of Hincks' friend, Robert W. Lloyd (1868–1958). Lloyd also bequeathed his personal collections of European beetles and butterflies

Above: Male and female of the giant earwig.

Right: Robert W. Lloyd, the merchant and philanthropist whose exceptional generosity allowed the Manchester Museum to acquire the unique collection of tortoise-beetles.

and his extensive library of rare and antiquarian entomological books to the Entomology Department. In addition, his fine collection of Japanese lacquer, ivories, metalwork and weapons was bequeathed to the Manchester Museum's Living Cultures department (see p. 50).

Of the more exotic insect groups, one might be surprised to know that the Manchester Museum possesses the most comprehensive earwig collection in the world, with more than 11,000 specimens representing 975 species, which is about half of the earwig species known worldwide. The original collection of the late W.D. Hincks was purchased by the Museum in 1961, and formed the nucleus of the earwig collection. It was subsequently significantly extended by Alan Brindle (1915–2001), Hincks' successor in the post of Keeper of Entomology and an outstanding entomologist himself, during the course of his extensive 30-year taxonomic research on earwigs. More importantly, Brindle improved the scientific quality of the Museum's earwig collection by adding type specimens of hundreds of new species he described. A species of special importance in this collection is the extinct giant earwig from the island of St Helena (see p. 91).

The scientific quality and international reputation of any natural history collection is measured by the number of deposited type specimens. A 'type specimen' (or 'type') is a reference specimen selected by a scientist during the description of a new species. Type specimens serve as the primary and unique references for all known species names. They play a key role in stabilizing the use of species names. The Entomology Department holds more than 12,000 type specimens representing some 2,500 species names of primarily foreign insects. This makes the Manchester Museum one of the most important entomological depositories in the UK.

Above: The holotype of *Pseudacanthus nigidioides*, a species of bess beetle described by W.D. Hincks in 1949.

" *I think my nine-year-old son would like to work here one day.* "

Museum visitor

Entomology

A lot of my research is on the interactions between plants and insects. One of the questions I ask is 'how does the variety of plant species in an area affect the variety of insects?' In the tropics those plant communities might consist of a few giant mahogany trees and all the thousands of epiphytes growing on them. In the UK the plant community of interest may be a wildflower meadow. In both cases we collect hundreds of thousands of insects on and around the plants and look to see how many species there are and how many individuals there are of each species. We use this information to make estimates of biodiversity, and these estimates are completely dependent on our ability to identify all of the insects that we collect. The reference collections in the Manchester Museum, and the expert knowledge of the curators who so diligently maintain those collections, are an invaluable resource for my research. For example, the discovery of a new species of beetle in the rainforest is only really possible once we can define what has previously been found and identified, and to do this requires the resources of a museum. The Manchester Museum represents a core asset of the University, one of those things so central to what we do that we sometimes forget how much we depend on the expertise it provides. Access to places like the Museum have enabled us to be the centre of learning that we have become.

Richard Preziosi
Senior Lecturer, Faculty of Life Sciences
University of Manchester

> *A herbarium is better than any illustration; every botanist should make one.*

Carl Linnaeus (1751)
[Translated Frans A. Stafleu (1971)]

All the green things upon the earth

The study of botany does not just cover the flowering plants which people are most familiar with, but also the cryptogams (the so-called 'lower-plants' including ferns, fungi, algae, lichens, mosses and liverworts). A herbarium is the name given to a collection of preserved plants, mostly as pressed specimens mounted on paper or in envelopes, although some may be preserved in alcohol. In addition, a herbarium can include larger specimens such as timbers, seeds and insect galls. Developing a herbarium was an occupation which was enthusiastically embraced by the botanists of Manchester from the 19th century into the early 20th century. They were driven not just by the desire to collect; they also wanted to improve their understanding of botany and to explore ideas about what grew where and why. Their extensive collections of dried botanical specimens now form the major part of the herbarium at the Manchester Museum.

Although members of the Manchester Society for the Promotion of Natural History were interested in botany, botanical collections did not figure very highly in the early years of the Museum. It wasn't until 1899 that the Museum hired its first dedicated Assistant Keeper of Botany, Harold Murray. The seeds of this increasing interest in the study of plants can be traced back to 1890, when the Museum moved to its present site, and became closely associated with Owens College. This was largely

95

through the efforts of William Crawford Williamson (1816–95), who was Professor of Natural History from 1851–79 and Professor of Botany between 1879 and 1892. He not only taught University students but also donated objects like model fruit for display in the Museum galleries. Models were important for allowing students and public visitors to see and understand the fine detail of plant and fungal structures. The beautiful models produced by Robert Brendel (*c.*1821–98) and his son Reinhold Brendel (*c.*1861–1927) in Breslau and Berlin were particularly prized for their accuracy and attractiveness.

In addition to lecturing, Williamson also gave classes to the general public on topics such as 'The Life History of the Moss'. At these popular public events, Williamson would give a scientific talk, followed by a practical demonstration of the topic, often using microscopes. It was at one such event that the 22-year-old Charles Bailey (1838–1924) was inspired to start creating his own herbarium. Charles Bailey moved to Manchester in 1852 when he began working for the Ralli Brothers, who were merchants of the East India Company. In the 1860s he started to buy examples of plants found growing in the UK and throughout Europe, including non-native plants (see text box opposite). He aimed to collect a specimen from as many different countries as possible to study the differences of climate on plant growth. He was so successful at building up his herbarium (over 3,000 boxes) that it required a separate building in which

Right: Oxford Ragweed (*Senecio squalidus*), a railway traveller.

Above: 19th-century anatomical teaching models of plants made by Brendel.

"*The herbarium is a fantastic place with lots of history and scientific value.*"

Museum visit

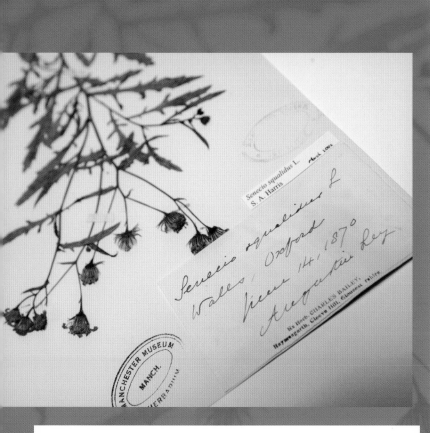

to house it. Ironically, the enthusiasm of collectors for rare species (especially for ferns and orchids) for their gardens or herbaria resulted in a decline in the wild population of these species, and even today over-collection is still a threat to rare species around the world.

As Bailey's interest was sparked by Manchester's Owens College, he decided that he would eventually leave his collection to the Manchester Museum. However, his friend James Cosmo Melvill was also a great collector of botanical specimens, and he too intended to leave his collection to the Museum. In order to make their herbaria more useful when

Above: These 14 specimens of Oblong Woodsia (*Woodsia ilvensis*) were collected in 1824, and over half include the roots. Populations of rare fern species were threatened by the enthusiasm of Victorian collectors for ferns – a phenomenon called 'Pteridomania'.

Unwanted intruders

From the 17th to the 19th centuries, British plant hunters were at their most active in scouring the world for interesting plants to bring home to collectors or sponsors. Some plants were chosen as they were new to science, others because they might prove to be useful, but most were brought back to satisfy the British fascination with gardening. One such plant is the Oxford ragweed (*Senecio squalidus*), which was collected from the stony slopes of Mt Etna, Sicily, and was first grown in British gardens in the 17th century. By 1792, this plant had escaped the garden and was to be found growing in the walls of the colleges in Oxford, but its big break came with the invention of the railways in the 19th century. The fly-away seeds with their parachute of fine hairs were able to drift along the railway lines, and found the tracks an ideal habitat in which to grow. Over the next 200 years it spread across the UK and is now a common sight on disturbed ground. The spread of these 'alien' plants can be documented through herbaria, and it is a topic which interested the collector Charles Bailey, whose herbarium contains many examples of these introduced curiosities.

"I think more people should see and appreciate the Herbarium!"

Museum visitor

they eventually came together in the collections of the Museum, Bailey and Melvill agreed that their donations would not overlap. So they split the world between them, with Bailey focussing on the UK and Europe and Melvill collecting plants from everywhere else.

James Cosmo Melvill (1845–1929) had been interested in plants from an early age and had written a guidebook, *The Flora of Harrow*, while still at school. He was the first of the pair to donate his collection, in 1904, and it was joined by Bailey's herbarium in 1917. When donated, Melvill's herbarium was estimated to contain 40,000 species, and was one of the three largest private herbaria in the country. The Museum Reports at the time show that they were delighted to receive it, as the Manchester Museum moved from having no botanical collection of note to having one of the most important collections outside London. Botany now deserved a space reflecting its new status: 'A special room in the top floor of the Museum has been provided with electric light and heating apparatus to ensure the collections are being kept dry.'

Like Bailey, Melvill was a Manchester businessman who built up his collection by buying from or exchanging specimens

Above: One of the oldest in the collection (18th century), a type specimen of *Pultenaea stipularis* (fine-leaved bush pea) collected in New South Wales, Australia from the herbarium of J.E. Smith.

Left: Charles Bailey bought many specimens from other collectors such as these careful preparations of mushrooms and toadstools made commercially in Germany by Gustav Herpell (1828–1912).

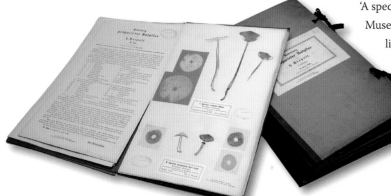

with other botanical collectors. As a result, his herbarium drew together material from other people's collections, including specimens collected by some famous names of botany, and these now form some of the treasures of the Museum's herbarium. For example, through Melvill, the Museum received a duplicate set of the Australian specimens of Sir James Edward Smith (1759–1828), who founded the Linnean Society in London in 1788, and which still supports biological research today. Forty-two of these specimens are 'types' which are examples collected when a previously unknown species is first described and named.

In the 19th century, there were many fans of ferns, mosses and liverworts around Manchester, such as William Wilson (1799–1871), John Nowell (1802–69) and Benjamin Carrington (1827–93), and all of them are represented in the herbarium. The moss (*Lepidozia chordulifera*, see photo on p. 100) is from Carrington's collections, and it was picked by Charles Darwin (1809–82), who later developed the theory of evolution through natural selection. It is one of the 20 specimens in the Manchester Museum herbarium which was collected on the second expedition of HMS *Beagle* (1831–6) and originated from the Chonos Archipelago in Chile.

Mother of the sea

Kathleen Drew-Baker (1901–57), a researcher in the Botany department at the University of Manchester, was an expert in the study of seaweeds (marine algae). In particular, she studied purple laver seaweed (*Porphyra umbilicalis*), working either with specimens from the seashore near her holiday cottage in North Wales, or in a custom-built experimental seawater tank in her lab in Manchester. In 1949, this work was published in the science journal *Nature*, describing a missing step in the life-cycle of purple laver. This missing step is found growing on and burrowing into the surface of shells, and had previously been wrongly identified as an entirely different species of alga (*Conchocelis rosea*). Across the globe in Japan, the potential importance of this study was swiftly recognised. New experiments soon confirmed the same life-cycle in the related species *Porphyra tenera*, better known as *nori*, the seaweed often wrapped around sushi. At the time, *nori* was harvested from natural seaweed populations which were threatened by environmental disasters, but the understanding of how to 'seed' areas with new plants transformed *nori* production into a thriving industry. Following Drew-Baker's untimely death, the Japanese wished to honour her, and so on 14 April 1963, a memorial was unveiled in Sumiyoshi Shrine Park in Tokyo. Every year since, a ceremony is held on 14 April to thank the Shinto gods for helping this 'Mother of the Sea'.

Below: *Porphyra* species with *Conchocelis rosea* attached to a shell.

This local interest in cryptogamic botany resulted in the herbarium being particularly rich in these kinds of plants, and for many decades the University of Manchester was a centre for their study (see p. 95). The Museum also has a good number of type specimens amongst the cryptogams. For example, the Museum received the personal collection of the Amazonian and Andean explorer Richard Spruce (1817–93) via the donation of another local enthusiast W.H. Pearson (1849–1923). His collection contains 8,971 liverworts, including over 900 type specimens along with maps of his travels and letters to friends and scientists.

The third of the largest additions to the Museum herbarium was that of Leo Grindon (1818–1904), donated by his wife Rosa in 1910. Consisting of approximately 10,000 herbarium sheets, the Grindon collection is very different to the other herbaria of wild plants. Firstly, Grindon

Above: Artefacts from the explorer Richard Spruce, including hand-drawn maps of uncharted areas, letters and type specimens of liverworts.

Below: Moss *Lepidozia chordulifera* collected from the Chonos Archipelago, Chile, by Charles Darwin in 1834 while travelling with HMS *Beagle*. From the herbarium of Benjamin Carrington.

focused on cultivated plants, writing in 1885 that: 'The natural character of a plant is that which it is capable of becoming. This is very generally declared only by cultivating it…. I prefer a good garden specimen, beautifully dried, to a dismal and uninviting mummy from the native land.' The second difference is that, along with the preserved plant specimens, Grindon included botanical illustrations, cuttings from newspapers, articles from gardening magazines and even reviews of his own talks. This herbarium formed the basis of Grindon's botanical teaching, containing information on what a plant looks like, how long it has been cultivated, how to grow it and what it can be used for. Initially a cashier for a Manchester firm, he was enthusiastic about educating adults and improving the lives of working families through gardening and the appreciation of nature. He wrote a number of popular books on botany and later became a lecturer at the University of Manchester.

Above: Leopold Hartley Grindon (1818–1904). He encouraged the working class people of Manchester to grow flowers to make their lives less bleak.

Right: Grindon herbarium sheet of ornamental slipper orchid illustrations (*Cypridium* species).

Other substantial, important and interesting collections such as those from the Salford Museum, the Material Medica or the personal collection of J.N. Mills (1914–77) continued to arrive in the Manchester Museum. However, the structure and organisation of the herbarium still owes much to the large donations from Bailey, Melvill and Grindon. Today the herbarium is the fifth largest in the UK, and is estimated to contain approximately 750,000 specimens. It is currently not only valuable as a historic document but also as a resource for scientific study, artistic inspiration and teaching.

> "*Many thanks – the Mills [herbarium] material is priceless.*"
>
> Tim Rich, National Museum Cardiff

Below: Several jars from the Materia Medica collection which originally formed a display in the pharmacy department, and demonstrates natural sources of medicines.

Herbarium

The Manchester Museum herbarium is one of my favourite places on campus, where I can spend hours and hours. From the very moment when you open the door of the herbarium the smell of the old specimens, which can only be accumulated over decades and

centuries, welcomes you, reminding you that you are entering a very special place. The next thing that will follow is sheer surprise at the impressive volume of the collection behind the quaint Victorian façade. The genuine love for science in the past found in the herbarium never fails to inspire. Inspiration such as this benefits young students who will lead science in the future and helps engage the general public with scientific issues. The herbarium is also an invaluable resource for a broad range of biology disciplines. As a biologist who studies plant evolution and development, I constantly use herbarium specimens for my research. The advantages of using these specimens is that they have been collected from all over the world over a long period of time, and they are taxonomically identified and grouped. This makes some 'impossible' research 'possible'. For example, we have been recording and tracing the evolution of the leaf shapes of about 2,000 fern species from herbarium specimens. Without them, this project would not be possible, because we cannot visit all the places where collections were made and few people in the world can identify 2,000 fern species. The herbarium is a great heritage we all should appreciate, and at the same time an invaluable scientific resource that should be exploited more actively. And for me, it is definitely the place where I wish to spend my spare time when I retire someday.

Minsung Kim
Lecturer, University of Manchester

Simply looking at a frog has always seemed to me to be just about the most interesting thing there is.

David Attenborough (2010)

Live animals, conservation through education

Opposite: The Red-eyed Leaf Frog (*Agalychnis callidryas*), Costa Rica.

Below right: Professor H. Graham Cannon, founder of the Cannon Aquarium, in 1963.

The history of displaying live animals in aquaria and vivaria dates back to the first public Aquarium in London in 1826. However, today it still remains quite unusual to find live reptile and amphibian displays in a museum, something many people rather associate as belonging in a zoo. Although some comparisons can perhaps be made, and the Museum holds a zoo licence, the vivarium at the Manchester Museum is quite different from any zoo. Whereas zoos have grown mainly from a background primarily of entertainment, live collections in museums have grown from quite different rootstock, that of education and research. The vivarium at Manchester is no different to this, and first started as a teaching resource developed 50 years ago by the University's Zoology Department.

First opened in 1963, the live collection at the Manchester Museum was named 'The Cannon Aquarium', after Professor H. Graham Cannon (1897–1963), the then Head of Zoology. Professor Cannon's research interests focused on fish behaviour, and he initially started the aquarium in the Museum to enable his students to study a wide range of these in captivity. Professor Cannon was a graduate of Cambridge University, and took his first chair at Sheffield University before moving to Manchester. Here he became a popular medical lecturer at a time when the study of comparative anatomy was key in providing a basis for evolutionary studies.

105

Over the years, the aquarium slowly developed to include reptiles and amphibians. These became increasingly popular with the many schoolchildren that visited the Museum, and during the 1970s to early 1990s the aquarium and vivarium contained an eclectic selection of different animal types. These had been obtained from a wide variety of different sources, including seizures by HM Customs, exchanges with Belle Vue Zoo, and donations from the public. Some of the strangest acquisitions at this time ranged in size from baby alligators and crocodiles to huge African snakes, which much to the public and schoolchildren's delight at the time, were regularly fed live rodents while on display. Husbandry practices and animal housing at this time were not ideal, and some of these animals had to be re-homed quite regularly, often requiring special man-handling and transportation to more substantial enclosures elsewhere. By 1995 there was only one solitary live piranha fish to be found in the aquarium-based displays at Manchester. This single fish, having systematically devoured all its tank mates, was eventually re-housed to Bolton Museum's aquarium, to spend the rest of its days in a larger and more suitable aquarium.

Left: Aquarist Jim Whitworth and members of the Belle Vue Zoo staff transport an alligator from the vivarium, c.1970.

Right: Madagascan Day Gecko (*Phelsuma madagascariensis*), a beautiful diurnal lizard on public display.

"We have made many trips to the Museum over the years and the highlight for our family is always the frogs. We feel very proud that a North-West museum is raising such environmental awareness: You are true ambassadors!"

The Dean family

Above: A rare Splendid Leaf Frog, captive-bred at the Manchester Museum for the first time in the world.

A splendid frog indeed

In the wild, the beautiful Splendid Leaf Frog (*Cruziohyla calcarifer*) can only be found in a few untouched primary rainforest areas between Guatemala and Ecuador. It was first described in 1902, but until fairly recently there were only 20 dead specimens in museums worldwide. Working closely with the relevant authorities, the Museum was the first institution to be given special permission to collect and acquire live specimens from the wild. This made it possible to study the species for the first time, and one new discovery made was the intricate way these frogs communicate to one another – using unusual leg-waving behaviour never seen before. An extremely rare species, it was also bred in captivity for the first time in the world at the Manchester Museum as a vital part of the effort to ensure its preservation. Forty specimens have been bred at Manchester and distributed to zoos worldwide as a safety net in case wild populations decline, but thanks to recent in-country conservation work it is no longer threatened with extinction in the wild for the foreseeable future.

In the year 2000, the keeping of live animals at the Manchester Museum was completely reviewed. After much consultation, it was decided that if the collection could be fully focused on highlighting issues such as sustainability and wildlife conservation then a new vivarium would indeed have a leading role to play in supporting the future goals of this university museum. As such, the vivarium was completely redesigned, and moved from its original third-floor position in the 1885 building to the second floor, where unusual reptiles and amphibians would form the main focus. Large, purpose-built exhibits were newly created, and although the new gallery covered roughly the same amount of floor-space as the old aquarium, rather than 24 exhibits it now contained less than half the amount. However, these ten exhibits were much larger, with floor-to-ceiling cases, incorporating the latest specialist heating, lighting, and humidity control equipment to create the optimum living environments for a new generation of reptiles and amphibians. The gallery design and the visual interpretation were also aimed at providing the best possible access for all age ranges and abilities of visitors.

The Manchester Museum's vivarium is now one of the most popular and distinctive of all the Museum's galleries. Dedicated to the display and study of live reptiles and amphibians, the vivarium contains over 30 species from South America, Australia, and Madagascar. Nowhere else in Manchester can visitors experience first-hand the beauty and thrill of encountering so many of the planet's rarest creatures. Vivarium staff, which include the Curator of Herpetology and his two assistants, are fully dedicated to providing the best possible care for the animals. Over the past ten years the Museum has won awards for its animal husbandry practice, including a prestigious special award given in 2002 by the Universities Federation for Animal Welfare

(UFAW) that assesses best practice in all zoo-licensed premises throughout the UK. This award provided particular recognition with respect to the Museum's Rainforest Exhibit. Such awards are only made in special recognition of those exhibits that allow the animals to live in good health, with as near a natural life-style as possible. As with all of the new exhibits in the vivarium, the addition of live plants and a mix of naturally occurring animals within all the exhibits create a near-natural ecosystem. As was recognized, this enables the species maintained to have the opportunity to behave and breed naturally, and some of those being kept at the Manchester Museum have bred for the very first time ever in captivity (see text box on p. 107).

The vivarium is active in contributing to species conservation in several ways, including raising public awareness of the issues surrounding biodiversity and sustainability through a myriad of engagement activities, and by directly taking part in international breeding programmes for endangered species. The public displays continue to give visitors an opportunity to see a different side to reptiles and amphibians, two unusual groups of animals which often get a very bad press through the media, and which sometimes have a negative public image. Experiencing these creatures first-hand excites and creates such an interest for many of our visitors, and we hope this may lead them to a future care and commitment to not only the animals, but also to helping protect the environment where they naturally occur.

Many of the children who visit the Museum from the surrounding areas are treated to a unique learning experience with the Museum's unusual live animals. Special handling collections have been developed specifically to facilitate the new teaching sessions and the objects used in these collections range from a wide variety of amazing creatures that show some remarkable adaptations. Numerous local community groups and organisations also enjoy the educational, emotional, and therapeutic benefits of being able to experience the animals at close quarters. Sessions include working with groups of children with autistic spectrum disorder and also support continued learning in older people from such groups as Probus.

Opposite: Eye to eye – Many of the Museum's creatures used for teaching have unusual adaptations which children find fascinating.

Left: The award-winning 'South American Rainforest' exhibit features as centrepiece of the vivarium displays.

Below: Boy enjoys 'hands-on' experience with rare male Fijian Iguana (*Brachylophus fasciatus*).

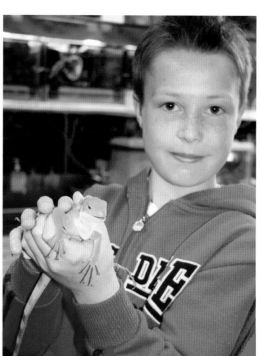

Apart from curatorial staff, the vivarium also has a small team of volunteers, consisting mainly of zoology and biology students from the Faculty of Life Sciences at the University of Manchester. Apart from helping maintain the animals, on a daily basis our volunteers also assist with our live animal 'hands-on' table, which allows all our visitors a first-hand experience. All our volunteers are valued members of our team and we hope that the experience they receive while working with us and the animals is enjoyable, and goes some way to helping support their chosen course and their future profession.

The vivarium is particularly notable for its large collection of neotropical leaf frogs, and the Museum has been responsible for establishing important captive breeding programmes for some of the world's most critically endangered species. One example of this is

'Extinct' frog rediscovered

In 2007, a critically endangered frog thought to be extinct was rediscovered by the Museum's Curator of Herpetology, Mr Andrew Gray. After receiving special permission from the Costa Rican authorities to work in the famous Monteverde Cloud Forest Preserve, he went on a mission to find rare frogs. A significant crash in the amphibian population occurred at Monteverde in the late 1980s, when many species disappeared without trace, including the Golden Toad (*Bufo pereglines*). Here, a changing climate and serious fungal pathogen was considered to be responsible. The beautiful brown and metallic-green treefrog re-discovered was *Isthomhyla rivulari*, a species that had disappeared from Monteverde along with the Golden Toad 20 years ago, and no-one had seen it since. After taking several unique photographs, he released the little frog exactly where it had been found. This significant find excited biologists and conservationists around the globe, many of whom have been searching for such a species at Monteverde themselves. It also provided new hope that other species considered to be extinct, such as the Golden Toad, may too have survived, and await similar discovery. A recent project to help conserve endangered frogs at Monteverde, through health screening and population monitoring, was initiated by the Museum and is being carried out through collaboration with Chester Zoo.

Right: The treefrog (*Isthmohyla rivularis*) rediscovered in Costa Rica.

the programme initiated for the Lemur Leaf Frog, one of the world's most critically endangered amphibians. Live specimens of this species maintained at the Manchester Museum are from the last remaining population in Costa Rica, which are on the very brink of extinction. In 2001 the Manchester Museum initiated the first captive breeding programme for this species, and over the years 400 young bred at the Museum have been distributed to national and international zoos, including Bristol Zoo, the Vancouver Aquarium, Canada, and the Atlanta Botanical Gardens in the USA. Leaf frogs exhibit unusual characteristics and behaviours that set them apart from many amphibians, and maintaining them in captivity has provided many new research opportunities to investigate them that would otherwise have been impossible. Curatorial staff are highly involved with supporting amphibian-related research that aims to provide a much better understanding of the animals, help in their captive care, and specifically aid their conservation. All the research work is completely non-invasive and normally combines

field studies with captive observations. On an annual basis curatorial staff also supervise a variety of undergraduate and graduate student research projects in the Department and sometimes abroad, as well as leading research expeditions to remote areas of the world to search for and work with rare frogs.

Over the past few years the Curator of Herpetology has been working closely with professionals in the media, who share our interest in providing people with a positive and highly educational view of the animals concerned. He has worked with the BBC on several David Attenborough *Life* series, including 'Life in Cold Blood' and 'Human Planet', and acted as main scientific advisor on the programme 'Jungles' for the award winning series *Planet Earth*. Such series have done much to heighten people's awareness and interest in the natural world, and the Museum is very pleased to be associated with them.

Above: Vivarium volunteer with male Panther Chameleon (*Furcifer pardalis*).

Left: Giant Monkey Frog (*Phyllomedusa bicolour*), just one of the vivarium's animals filmed for educational purposes and featured in the David Attenborough *Life* series for the BBC.

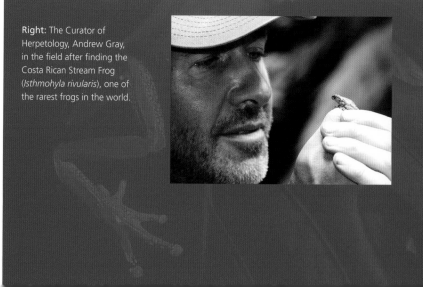

Right: The Curator of Herpetology, Andrew Gray, in the field after finding the Costa Rican Stream Frog (*Isthmohyla rivularis*), one of the rarest frogs in the world.

Vivarium

The Manchester Museum vivarium is a wonderful place to visit and inspires the visitor with the variety of life. I love visiting the living specimens, which are beautifully and sensitively displayed. I am heavily involved in teaching in the Faculty of Life Sciences, and the vivarium offers a unique learning experience for our undergraduate students to interact first-hand with living organisms. I organise a practical for 180 first-year students where they get the opportunity to visit the Museum for a session called 'Animal adaptations to diverse environments'. Close examination and handling of the live animals enables the students to gain a deeper understanding of animal characteristics, classification and adaptation. Uniquely it provides them with the opportunity to compare the adaptation of animals using a variety of live amphibians and reptiles. Judging by comments such as 'reminds me why I like biology' and 'makes it real', it is no surprise that this is one of the most popular practicals in the first year.

Amanda Bamford
Senior Lecturer, Faculty of Life Sciences
University of Manchester

Below: Lemur Leaf Frog (*Agalychnis lemur*) showing night colouration, a critically endangered species on the very brink of extinction.

" *I recently popped into the Manchester Museum and was grabbed by the vivarium displays. They were without doubt the best displays I have seen, and I have been an amateur herpetologist all my life.* "

Russell Richardson

> *Conservation is the technology by which preservation is achieved.*
>
> Philip Ward (1986)

Investigating and preserving the collections

10

The conservation department at the Manchester Museum was formed in 1975 to care for the Museum's many objects and to protect them for future generations to enjoy and understand. The Museum has around four million objects, which are either on display in the galleries, in storage or out on loan. As can be seen from the chapters in this guide they are drawn from the natural world, antiquity and human cultures from many parts of the world. They vary in countless ways, such as material, size, age and fragility, and present many different challenges for conservation during their treatment but also opportunities for hidden secrets to be revealed. By 1978 the conservation department was run by Velson Horie. There were also three Museum technicians: Don Ashton (Archaeology), Roy Garner (Zoology) and Bill Hutchinson who worked across the collection (see text box on p. 116). The first treatment record cards for the department date back to the late 1940s, though we now store our conservation documentation and photographs on the Museum's computer database.

The department is situated in the new wing of the Museum and consists of two large rooms that can accommodate all but the biggest objects that need treatment, and smaller rooms which house freezers (for treating pest outbreaks), fume cupboards and storage for objects in the course of being treated. There is a large goods lift which opens into the department and allows objects to be brought to and from the galleries and the stores.

Above: Main conservation studio of the Manchester Museum.

I think it was a superb idea and is just plain awesome, because it shows us how different materials degrade.

Barbar Khan (12 years old), Matthew Moss High School

An object may need treating because it is deteriorating or it may need cleaning so that its surface and form can be appreciated by visitors. As materials have different chemical properties and characteristics it is important that the conservator discovers as much information as possible about an individual object to inform the treatment, and this part of the process is often done in collaboration with the curators.

The conservator needs to know about the life of the artefact before it entered the Museum and what has happened to it since it has become part of the collection, as this often gives clues about its condition, its use and its history. It is this information that helps a conservator plan treatments such as cleaning, repair or strengthening. Part of the skill that a conservator has to perfect is to understand what is original to an object and when it is necessary to clean down to the 'original' surface, removing dirt and not removing anything of importance. Cleaning often takes place under microscopes.

Much of the department's time is spent preparing objects to go on display or to go out on loan to other museums or art galleries. When an object goes out on loan there is a great deal of preparation involved, ensuring that the object is safe to travel and checking that the conditions will be safe for the object during its stay in another venue. Moving an object can be a hazardous time for large or fragile objects, and it is crucial that any move is meticulously planned. This can take weeks of planning for the bigger and heavier objects or large groups of objects.

Above: Egyptian relief being cleaned under a microscope.

Below left: Maharajah the elephant's ribcage during conservation.

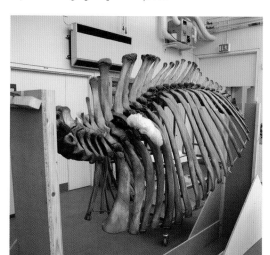

114

Conservation staff have always been on hand when the mummies have been transported to the Manchester Royal Infirmary or the Dental Hospital for medical examination. In less restrictive conditions in the mid 1970s one of the conservation team (Roy Garner) once stood in a lead-lined jacket, with his arm around the mummy Asru, whilst she had her teeth scanned. Now, because of stricter health and safety rules and technological advances, a mummy would be laid on a supportive mount and manoeuvred through the latest scanning or x-ray equipment automatically.

Conservation often enlists the help of colleagues who have access to analytical equipment to help build a picture of the object and an understanding of how it may have been made and what materials were used.

The Museum houses a large proportion of the collection in stores which are segregated by material. The environments are maintained to provide a stable temperature and humidity which is suitable for that particular collection. Sensors in the stores monitor the temperature and humidity and these feed back readings to a computer in the conservation laboratory; by controlling these we can keep the specimens in the best conditions, so that they do not get too dry, damp, cold or hot. Controlling the environments is crucial for the objects, as poor environments can cause permanent damage and changes to objects. These alterations can be seen when objects become discoloured or change physically and chemically. In extreme cases surfaces can become friable and the objects can start to fall apart, causing important evidence to be lost, such as carved detail on stone sculpture.

The original wing of the Museum was designed by Alfred Waterhouse in 1885, at which time an innovative environmental control system was installed in the building. There was a coal furnace, which produced hot air which was circulated throughout the building by a large fan (approximately 2.5m in diameter). The air was pumped through the hollow columns which run the height of the 1885 building. This warm air was then released through vents/grids at the top of the seats on each floor. Summer ventilation was provided by opening vents at the top of the roof light, controlled by a large handle which was situated in the botany store. Natural daylight was controlled by stripped blinds on the windows. The display case doors had complicated hinges and door edges which had velvet linings that reduced air exchange and dust entering the cases. By 1900 the blinds had split and been removed, the fan had been replaced with water-fed radiators; gas flare lighting was installed, which produced condensation and the velvet had powdered away. This lack of protection from light can be seen in the early photograph of the Egyptian collection on display (see image on p. 37). It wasn't until the late 1970s that blinds were reintroduced as a protective measure to stop the strong sunlight fading the objects in the display cases. The main reason we keep light levels

Below: Objects stored by material in the archaeology store. The glass has been laid out as a trial for a new display.

115

Right: Light damage can be seen on this latex sheet that has degraded. The area that has been exposed to light has turned orange and become crystalline, whereas the area beneath the curl of latex has been partly protected from light and has not significantly changed in colour or texture.

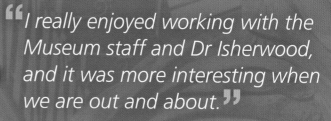

I really enjoyed working with the Museum staff and Dr Isherwood, and it was more interesting when we are out and about.

Michael Beardsley (12 years old), Matthew Moss High School

low in some of our gallery spaces is to shield them from exposure to strong sunlight which will fade and weaken the structure of organic artefacts.

Another critical environmental factor is the amount of humidity (water vapour) in the air. Too high a humidity level can cause moulds to grow on organic materials (such as leather, paper and textiles), causing irreversible staining, and too dry an environment can cause the same objects to dry and shrink beyond repair. For example, our vulnerable ancient metals collection needs to be kept very dry (below 35% relative humidity) to avoid active corrosion (changes to the metal's stable condition), which will destroy the object if it is not controlled. We make sure that we keep the store dry by using a

Above: Bronze blade suffering from bronze disease.

Cleaning the suspended whale

This whale skeleton came to Manchester along the Ship Canal in 1897 (see p. 79 for more details). In 1980 (83 years later), a scaffolding bridge was erected between the two galleries on either side, suspended 20ft in the air, to allow access to the whale skeleton in order to examine and clean it. The conservation took eight weeks in total. The 30ft whale was carefully dusted, vacuumed and had poultices applied to remove embedded dirt and excess oils, before being carefully rinsed to ensure that there was no further action from the cleaning agents. One of the most serious considerations was attending to the rusting wires that held the bones together, which can cause staining of the bones. If the corrosion had been advanced enough the wire could have rusted through, resulting in small parts of the skeleton dropping off. During the project any rusting wire was replaced with stainless steel to prevent this happening in the future. As was noticed by the conservator Roy Garner, who undertook the task, 'One of the things we were able to do was to scotch a bit of Museum folklore. The story was that "in the old days" the skeleton was given an annual rub-down with linseed oil! Our examination showed no sign of years of application of linseed oil – or anything else.' However, many objects in museums, galleries and country houses have been subjected to well-meaning housekeeping over the years. This is done to keep the collections 'clean' and presentable, which in some cases may have done no harm, but repetitive cleaning can cause damage and loss of surface information. As conservation methods have changed, scientific investigation has become routine, and the type of damage that can be caused by cleaning can be demonstrated through techniques such as microscopy. This understanding has led to less interventive treatments on objects being the norm and preferable and certainly routine cleaning is avoided – although a light dusting is sometimes essential!

Right: This taxidermy specimen of a rat was stripped of its fur many years ago by webbing clothes moths.

Below right: Getting close up and personal with one of the trapped pests caught in the museum.

Below: The conservator Roy Garner cleaning the whale's ribs.

dehumidifier which will extract the water out of the air until it reaches the right level for the objects.

Pest management is another vital part of collections management for museums, galleries and historic houses. The fur or feathers of a taxidermy specimen provide an ideal source of food for insects such as the webbing clothes moth (*Tineola bisselliella*), which feeds on the keratin in these materials. A dried plant specimen from the botany collection, meanwhile, could happily sustain an infestation of biscuit beetles (*Stegobium paniceum*), which thrive on starch. Preventing these insects from getting into the collections requires constant monitoring and inspections of the collection areas. Triangular sticky traps are placed around the building in order to detect insects, and the contents of these traps are checked regularly. Preventing pests coming into the Museum is our first priority and we do this by keeping a strict cleaning routine. This is one reason we encourage people not to eat in the gallery or in

As with all of the collections, we prepare artefacts for use in outreach sessions. We assess each object to make sure that it is suitable for these purposes and then prepare it, ensuring that it is made safe for handling sessions. The objects may need cleaning or repairing and they will often require a mount in order for them to travel and to prevent them from being damaged.

Many of our older taxidermy objects, which were prepared during the Victorian period, are not suitable for handling. This is partly because they may be fragile, but also because they would have been prepared using chemicals such as arsenic to clean and soften the skin. These, along with many of the botany specimens and anthropology objects, may also have been treated with other chemicals while in the Museum if they have suffered from pest damage or to kill off an infestation.

As conservators we are fortunate to work closely with the objects on a daily basis discovering and appreciating the diversity of the collection, but also being aware of our responsibility to safeguard the objects for the public and researchers of the future.

Left: Wrapped taxidermy specimens waiting to be frozen as a precautionary treatment before being re-installed on the Living Worlds Gallery.

Below: Conservator preparing natural history specimen for outreach session.

collection areas, as once the pests are in the space and the food leftovers have been consumed, the pests turn their attention to the objects. And infestations that go unnoticed or untreated can be extremely destructive. There are many different treatment methods for eradicating pests, such as freezing objects, heating them or putting them in an oxygen-free environment, and it is important that the treatment selected is appropriate to the type of material being treated.

Each of our Museum collections has different conservation issues. For example, the large collection of natural history specimens comes in many different forms: some specimens are mounted taxidermy, while others, especially birds, are kept just as the skins; some specimens are pickled in alcohol and kept in jars, whereas insects are kept pinned in drawers. Many of the plants in the herbarium are dried and pressed and mounted onto paper sheets. Natural history objects are very popular and the majority are kept in the basement stores, but as more and more of the collection is being used for events and exhibitions outside of the Museum, the conservation team tries to make these objects as accessible to the public as possible.

Conservation

The Manchester Museum preserves knowledge as objects, people and memories. It is a microcosm of the world. As a conservator, I aim to keep and increase this knowledge for people now and in the future. But we must manage the change of the objects, learning from the insights that gather around them. The first stage is understanding the object: what was its original significance, what is its importance now, and how will it be useful in the future? Conservation is applied material science – we need to know: what the object is made of, how it has changed, and how we can reduce or affect future changes. The materials of objects change over time in ways we do not fully understand. As part of the University, the Museum has led many advances in conservation research and applied these lessons in caring for its world-class collections. For instance, the natural history collections embody an irreplaceable history of changes in biodiversity across the world, and new users are asking new questions to address the challenges of global warming and globalisation. Methods that we use to maintain these objects need to evolve so that we do not distort the chemical and physical information they contain, even though those chemicals and structures have not yet been discovered. We therefore control the conditions in which we store, display and use the objects. The buildings, display cases and storage boxes reduce the effects of water, light, pollutants, vandals, pests and changes in relative humidity and temperature. These old, fragile, valuable objects are handled, maintained and restored where necessary, by experienced people. The Museum conserves its collections for widely diverse users, inspiring the wonder of a child or the next discovery of disease in Egypt, and is a centre of excellence in improving collection care for future generations.

Velson Horie
*Honorary Research Associate,
the Manchester Museum*

Using the collections

The belief that material display creates both knowledge and proper social relationships is a fundamental aspect of the European mentality.

Susan Pearce (1995)

Collection-based research

11

Previous pages: The stores house significantly more objects than can be seen on display. These are made accessible online, and are a major research resource. This image shows the Museum's Curator of Living Cultures, Stephen Welsh, in the ethnographic weapons store.

Opposite: A visiting researcher, David Penney (Faculty of Life Sciences), working with insect collections behind the scenes.

Right: Type specimen of the American Eider (*Somateria mollissima dresseri*) named after Henry Dresser (see p. 82). Shot in New Brunswick by a lighthouse keeper in 1863.

The collections of the Manchester Museum are huge, comprising around 4.5 million objects and specimens. They are officially 'Designated' by the government as being of national and international importance. For instance, the Museum's natural history collections retain more than 22,000 type specimens (the original specimens from which descriptions of new species are made), representing some 8,000 species names. This makes the Manchester Museum one of the most important taxonomic depositories in the UK. Similarly, the human cultures collections (Archaeology, Egyptology and Living Cultures) are in the top five in importance in the country, and, as the earlier chapters have shown, contain material of international significance.

With such large holdings, it is inevitable that the vast proportion of the Manchester Museum's collections (*c*.98%) is kept in storage, behind the scenes, and their full diversity will never be displayed. For many people, whose encounter with a museum is as a visitor to the galleries, or as a participant in a public event, it may seem strange that museums hold such large amounts of material without displaying it. We are sometimes asked why it is necessary to store all this 'stuff', and whether we could simply sell some of it.

The important point here is that museums have several inter-related functions. They exist to provide inspiration and enjoyment for people in the present, but they also exist to hold collections long-term, both for the use of researchers, and for future generations of people to enjoy. This 'repository' function of museums is much less evident and well-understood

than the display function, yet museums are one of the few institutions dedicated to preserving real material culture and specimens, which together with the documentation associated with them (notes and sketches from foreign expeditions, correspondence, information on collectors, details of provenance and context) form a unique archive for research, display and education.

Although modern digital technologies can offer us online access to collection-related information (see image on p. 147), museum objects and specimens have been and always will be some of the only physical proof and irreplaceable primary documentation of life on Earth or of past events – particularly for times before written records. It is only from the actual material itself that researchers can extract DNA or determine dates through radiocarbon analysis. It is because the questions we want to answer change over time, and the techniques available for analysis improve, that it is necessary to hold these large museum collections for the long term.

The Museum's collections are held on behalf of the public, which means that they belong to all of us. Because of this, Museum staff continuously support people to investigate and use the collection, whether they be children or adults, amateurs or professionals. The key to encouraging use of the collections is to let the world know what the Museum holds behind the scenes. The best way of doing this is to input information about the holdings into the Museum's collections database and making these records accessible and searchable via the Web. Museum staff and volunteers therefore spend much of their time on this relatively mundane but essential task.

Having found out what the Museum holds, the next step for many researchers is to contact the Museum's Resource Centre, which acts as a central, publicly visible area where anyone can book in to study, photograph and catalogue objects from the stored collections. It is used by academics, students, volunteers and members of the public for their research projects and for object-handling sessions. The Centre also hosts a number of volunteers who catalogue and photograph areas of the collections that have yet to be recorded on the Museum's online catalogue. Overall, the Centre receives some 1,000 visitors per year, many of them University of Manchester students, accessing the Museum collections as an integral part of their degree work. These come from a wide variety of courses, notably

Left: Mounted Barn Owl, dating from the early 20th century.

Below left: The Museum's collections are being databased and can be searched online via our website.

The hermit in the tower

In 2009, the Manchester Museum ran a groundbreaking project which challenged what it is to be a museum, why we have collections and the impact we are having on our planet. Ansuman Biswas, an internationally acclaimed artist, lived as a hermit in the Museum's Gothic tower for 40 days and nights. He had no contact with other people during his stay, but was in touch with the world through regular blog posts. His every move could be followed on a webcam in his tower hideaway. His aim was to delve into the Museum as a house of memory and to examine people's attitudes to loss and conservation. Each day a new object from the stores was presented on his blog as a stimulus for discussion and action. Objects ranged from a mosquito to a Maori cloak made out of kiwi feathers. The lively debate included proposals to give the objects back to their original owners, letting some species become extinct and destroying specimens (e.g. mosquitos). Members of the public were invited to comment on his proposals, and hundreds did so. The overwhelming response was that people really value the Museum's role in caring for collections on behalf of society, even those which are kept in store. The project highlighted some of the different ways collections are used, for example as a starting point for discussions with Manchester's diverse communities and forming a key part of university research.

Above: The Manchester Museum Hermit challenged the public to question the value of objects in the Museum from a glass jar of honey to a Maori cloak.

from Archaeology and Art History and the MA in Art Gallery and Museum Studies. Students from local colleges, art students and local art clubs are regular visitors, attracted by the well-lit space and the availability of interesting objects for drawing and photographing from the Museum's collections. Groups of local amateur geologists and historians are also regular users.

Each year, the Museum facilitates hundreds of research activities, many of them involving partnerships with other bodies. For instance, the Museum has been involved for several years in a research project on dinosaur locomotion, which draws on the Museum's collections and includes collaboration with the Natural History Museum, the University of Cambridge, the University of Liverpool and Manchester Metropolitan University, as well as six US and two European institutions.

The Museum's bird, botany and insect collections are widely consulted by experts worldwide, who are

Below: African archaeology workshop in the Museum's Resource Centre.

usually checking distributional records or examining particular species or groups of interest to their research. Interesting new uses which have emerged recently include: analysing the DNA in the bird and insect collections in order to more reliably identify and/or classify species; using the same collections for modern morphometrics studies which are aimed at understanding the evolutionary factors affecting body shape; and sampling the bird specimens for stable isotope analysis to study distribution and changes in diet over time.

There are numerous materials of particular scientific and cultural importance. For example, the Museum's building stone collection has been used by researchers to help put together English Heritage's Building Stone Atlas of Greater Manchester. Identifying the type of stone used and its place of origin in historical buildings is key to building conservation. Repairs need to be a close match to the original so that they look and weather in the same way. Specimens in the collection from some of Manchester's key buildings, such as the John Rylands Library, have labels that give information on the rock, the quarry and the company that supplied it.

Above: Field collecting is one of the ways natural history collections are acquired by the Manchester Museum. This image shows the Curator of Arthropods, Dmitri Logunov, collecting insects and spiders in larch taiga forest during his trip to northeast Siberia in 2002.

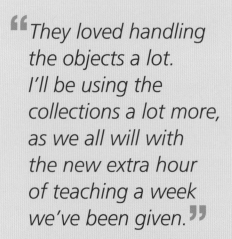

> **"**They loved handling the objects a lot. I'll be using the collections a lot more, as we all will with the new extra hour of teaching a week we've been given.**"**
>
> Dr Lindy Crewe, tutor, University of Manchester

Left: A selection of building stones from around the world, shedding light on some of Manchester's iconic buildings.

Above: Curator of Herpetology, Andrew Gray, using a live snake whilst teaching Manchester University Zoology students.

Strong efforts are made by Museum and University staff to encourage undergraduate and postgraduate students to use the Museum collections in their own projects and dissertations. Museum staff also assist in teaching courses, both within the University of Manchester and beyond, varying from Master's courses such as 'Science, Media and the Public' and 'Ancient World Studies' to first-year undergraduate courses such as 'Introduction to Palaeontology' or second-year courses such as 'Urban Biodiversity and Conservation'. The Manchester Museum is central to the University's on-line 'Certificate Course in Egyptology', which reaches students throughout the world, and uses the Museum's collections as a springboard for learning about Ancient Egypt. Museum curators are also actively involved in field courses run by the University, in hosting student visits to the collections, and in supervising student dissertations.

A wide variety of educational programmes have been developed based on the use of the live animal collection, and the age range that these cover spans from infants and early years children who visit the Museum to students at the University (see also p. 133). The animals are used in teaching sessions for all the zoology and biology students that come to Manchester. Also, several highly focused teaching sessions build on specific research collaborations with other University departments. One such example of this is the research that has focused on investigating the optical and thermoregulatory properties of amphibian skin, where a collaboration between the Museum and the University's Photon Science Institute has resulted in the development of

Above: One of the Museum's curatorial trainees, Gina Allnatt, helping with the entomological handling table during an Open Day at the University of Manchester.

Manchester, mummies and modern science

Since Margret Murray's scientific unwrapping of the mummies of the Two Brothers in 1908, the Manchester Museum has been synonymous with the study of ancient Egyptian human remains. Established in 1973, the Manchester Mummy Project pioneered non-destructive scientific techniques to examine mummified tissue. Information carried by mummies can be extracted to analyse aspects of ancient disease, diet, living conditions and the process of mummification itself. The project led to the creation in 1997 of the International Ancient Egyptian Mummy Tissue Bank, which collects and stores samples for further research. This in turn has yielded important insights into the pathology of diseases, which affect modern populations and were present in ancient Egypt. The mummy of Asru, a temple chantress during the Twenty-Fifth Dynasty (c.750–656 BC) (see figure on p. 35), was one of the first of the Project's many subjects. Asru was one of the Museum's first acquisitions from Egypt. She proved an ideal patient because she had so many ailments during life, which were evidenced in her remains. These included a parasitic bladder infection called schistosomiasis (also known as bilharzia), a worm infection in her intestines and lung disease. The Mummy Project was led by Rosalie David, who assembled an interdisciplinary team including pharmacists, biochemists, histologists, endoscopists, and even entomologists to identify the insects found in the mummy wrappings. David was the Museum's Egyptology curator between 1971 until her appointment as director of the University of Manchester's KNH Centre for Biomedical Egyptology in 2003. Research at the Centre remains ongoing, using samples from the Museum's collections. The more recently established Ancient Egyptian Animal Bio Bank has been created to analyse mummified animal species, which survive in abundance and were given as offerings to the gods at temples during the Late Period (c.750–30 BC).

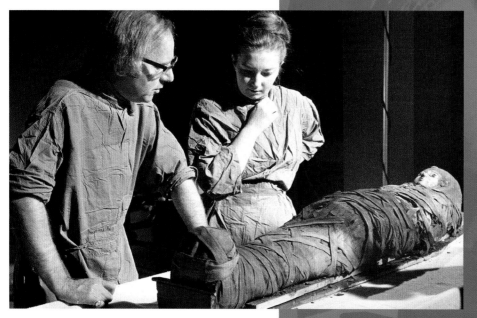

Left: Rosalie David and Eddie Tapp, members of the Manchester Mummy Project, unwrap Mummy 1770.

Above: These microscopic algae, called diatoms, are some of the most abundant organisms on Earth. They are an important barometer of climate change.

a joint teaching session for visiting A-level students from local Manchester colleges. These take place both in the Museum and in the adjacent Physics Department, and involve using a wide range of cutting-edge technology and equipment to explore a unique infra-red reflecting pigment found in the skin of tropical frogs from the Museum's live collection.

The Manchester Museum, in partnership with other British museums, is regularly involved in projects to provide trainee curatorial positions both in the natural sciences and the humanities. Such training is crucial for developing the necessary skills in a new generation of curators and curatorial assistants, and the expertise of staff in the Museum, along with the breadth of its collections, make it a natural centre for providing this kind of experience. The regional role played by the Museum also means that its staff frequently mentor colleagues from other museums wishing to deepen their knowledge.

The Manchester Museum regularly lends out material from its collections to other institutions for exhibition and to researchers in universities in this country and throughout the world. Overall, 50 to 100 loans totalling hundreds or even thousands of objects and specimens are borrowed each year, ranging from unidentified insects sent to overseas specialists to

"It is the best museum in the world. The best is the Egyptian part."

Museum visitor

Below: Museum leaflets for the Lindow Man exhibition marketing campaign.

Finding the treasures of Alderley Edge

In 1991 the writer Alan Garner presented to the Museum an old wooden shovel. Victorian miners had found it on Alderley Edge in 1875, but then it disappeared again. When he rediscovered it in 1953 no-one believed him that it was 4,000 years old, but radiocarbon dating proved that it was from the Bronze Age, made about 1750 BC. Then in 1995 the Derbyshire Caving Club, who lease the Alderley mines from the National Trust, uncovered a pot full of Roman coins from 330–40 (see picture). Perhaps the stories of early mining on the Edge were true after all. So the National Trust and the Museum together set up the Alderley Edge Landscape Project to study every part of Alderley Edge's story, from its creation in geological time to the coming of the railway and the first villas in 1842 and beyond, from natural history to social history, and of course to examine the legend of the king sleeping under the Edge. The Trust needed the information to create a proper management plan, and for the Museum – the only truly multidisciplinary department in Manchester University – it was a golden opportunity to bring all its academic resources together on a single research project. In fact the Edge was too complex for us to handle on our own, and many other specialists were called in, along with people from the village with their special local knowledge. Out of this came an exhibition, lectures, open days, an educational website (www.alderleyedge. manchester.museum), three excavations, and articles and books. The Museum's collections gained too – not just the archaeological finds, the coins and an archive of papers and recorded memories, but also minerals, insects and botanical specimens, even two species of bramble previously unknown to science.

Above: Rachel Bailey holding the pot with the coins on the day it was discovered by her father in 1995.

stone implements from cave deposits. The bulk of the loans out in any one year are of natural sciences material lent to researchers for further study (mosses or insects in particular), but humanities collections loans can be quite sizeable as well, for example when a specialist wishes to study the fabric of different kinds of pottery from Roman Manchester. These research loans are part of the 'behind the scenes' work the Museum undertakes to support the use of stored collections. These parallel the smaller number of more visible loans for temporary exhibitions to regional, national and even international museums.

Despite the range and size of its collections the Museum itself frequently borrows material from other institutions for its temporary exhibitions. For example, the Museum has a long-term strategic partnership with the British Museum, in which the latter lends some of its nationally important collections so that they can be seen and enjoyed by North-West audiences. The famous Lindow Man prehistoric bog body, discovered near Manchester in 1984, and normally housed at the British Museum, has been lent to the Manchester Museum a total of three times. The last time was in 2008–9 for a temporary exhibition in which the body was supported by a selection of other nationally important Iron Age material from the British Museum collection. It attracted over 160,000 visitors and won the Design Week best temporary exhibition award and the British Archaeological Award for innovation.

Museum staff are consulted constantly by researchers from around the world, and are linked to global networks of colleagues in universities, museums and related organisations. They frequently attend national and international conferences, often as keynote speakers, to talk about the Museum's collections and practice, and the research stimulated by them.

I would like to propose that we let the imagination take its place at the heart of learning, and that we create a climate in which it can flourish. We need discovery, making, doing, exploring, creating, critical thinking, seeing, hearing, experiencing.

Michael Morpurgo (2010)

Making sense of our world: learning from collections

Opposite: Learning from Egyptian objects at the Manchester Museum.

Below: Hands-on: 'Dinosaur explorer' workshop for primary schools.

Creative learning is central to the Museum's work encouraging people to explore and understand the natural world and other cultures past and present. Nowhere is this more so than in its work with schoolchildren, students and educators.

The Manchester Museum set out to be primarily an educational institution. From the First World War, it focused to a large extent on primary schools, in part as a response to local circumstance and wider educational policy. In Manchester, school buildings became military hospitals and the city implemented a 'two shift' system, enabling half a day to be spent off-site. Manchester's Education Committee approached the Museum to become a new site for these half days and developed classes (natural history and Egyptology) led by specialist teachers, funded by the Committee. In addition to this, the 1918 Education Act actively encouraged museum education. In 1954 the Children's Museum Club was set up – a travelling loans service across schools in the city – and by 1981, a dedicated Education Department consisting of six teachers, two clerical staff, a technician and a caretaker had use of two dedicated teaching spaces in the Museum. The Museum housed Local Education Authority teachers throughout the 20th century until funding was withdrawn in the early 1990s. By

133

this stage, visits by schools and colleges were part of the everyday life at the Museum.

Today, the Museum receives over 30,000 visits per year from school-age children. Creative learning in the Museum responds to and enriches the curriculum, is object-based, explores varied stories and interpretations and often encourages a tactile and imaginative approach to collections and environments. Primary schoolchildren still visit the Museum in their thousands. During these visits, they might journey back to 1925 to an Egyptologist's storeroom for archaeological training, explore the variety of life, habitats and how animals adapt to their surroundings or become dinosaur detectives, learning some of the skills of palaeontology to help solve a dinosaur murder mystery.

In recent years, the Museum has developed a strong reputation for its work with the very young. Through exploratory activities and workshops, the Museum has become a site for curiosity and imagination, story and play for the under-5s and their parents and carers. 'Magic Carpet' storytelling and activity sessions transport toddlers to other worlds, object-handling workshops encourage language and communication skills and the Museum as a whole provides a stimulating environment for exploration, wonder and awe.

Children and young people are encouraged to respond and express their opinions, thoughts and emotions through debates, workshops, writings and performance. Much of the Museum's work with secondary schools and post-16 students seeks

Above: School group in the Museum classroom, c.1980.

Top left: Children recording their finds in the archaeologist store in the exhibition 'Unearthed'.

Below: Snake handling in the 'Early years Animal Explorer' workshop.

Museum harvests own vegetables

The Manchester Museum's gallery 'Living Worlds' (see text box on p. 17) explores the connections between all living things, including us, and shows how we can all shape the future by the choices we make. One of the choices we can make is to grow food – on our windowsills, in our gardens, in our schools or even on an allotment. From May 2011 to October 2012 the Manchester Museum created an allotment outside its front entrance. It was created by volunteers, visitors, community groups, University scientists, students and Museum staff. Some of us know lots about gardening and many of us are beginners – so this project was all about sharing skills and a love of the outdoors. From our extraordinary 17th-century watering can and dried pea plants found on the banks of the River Mersey, to Ancient Egyptian farming tools and garden insects, there were lots of links with the Museum's collections. All good allotments have sheds, and in our shed visitors could find out about other local gardening and food projects and let us know what they think. The project was really rewarding – there were activities including planting, watering and eating plants, watched wildlife in the space, and even a vegetable orchestra. Volunteers met each week to tend the garden, children helped with watering cans, and in the summer we held student socials in the sun.

to develop enquiry skills and generate awareness and discussion of ethical issues in the Museum, for example how to display human remains. The Museum employs writers, artists, academics and dramatists to work with children and young people, enabling new ways to interpret and animate the collection, and also offering students the opportunity to meet people working in these fields and understand more about how these wider issues impact on everyday work and politics. Creative learning is often interdisciplinary in its approach, creating new connections and understanding.

'Real World Science', an acclaimed national programme, developed with other leaders in

Right: The Museum's allotment.

natural science education (including the Natural History Museum in London and Oxford University Museums) looks at how science works in real life with real scientists. The Manchester Museum works in partnership with University staff and postgraduate researchers to engage secondary school and post-16 science students. For example, in 'Nature's Palette', students investigate the different roles of colour in nature, from camouflage to attracting mates. They explore the physical and biological context of colour in the natural world by using case studies from scientists, real Museum specimens and independent research in the galleries.

The Museum's approach to creative learning is not focused solely on schoolchildren and students. The

> "A trip to the Manchester Museum is … holding a friend's hand, talking to someone new, going through a secret door, finding a snake, marvelling at an owl, drawing a fox, writing a label, counting the claws, holding a torch, spending time with dad."
>
> Darren Micklewright, classteacher of 3–4 year olds

Left: A-level geology student getting a close look at an ammonite fossil, during one of the Museum's geology master classes.

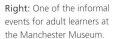

Right: One of the informal events for adult learners at the Manchester Museum.

Museum's commitment to lifelong learning is explored in more detail in the following section. The knowledge and expertise of researchers, curators and University staff is shared through formal learning programmes, as well as masterclasses, study days and specialist tours and lectures for adult learners. In addition to a wide range of University teaching, the Museum works in partnership with a series of adult learning providers to deliver courses, classes and workshops which draw upon the collections, exhibitions and resources of the Museum. Alongside these specialist activities, there are a range of introductory tours and informal events for adult learners, including film screenings and photography workshops.

The Museum works closely with teachers and tutors to develop imaginative, relevant and creative training programmes, learning activities, resources and teaching at all levels. Teachers and their students test-drive resources, pilot workshops and provide an insight into how museum-based learning might be embdedded into the existing curriculum and plans. Trainee and qualified teachers work with specialist Museum staff to develop their skills in object-based learning, critical thinking and communication skills as well as subject or curriculum-specific topics.

Whether in the Museum or off-site (as part of its learning outreach service to schools); whether hands-on, through close observation or dialogue; whether as teacher, pupil or adult learner, creative learning in the Manchester Museum invites us to reconsider and make sense of our world.

Tell me and I forget. Teach me and I remember. Involve me and I learn.

Benjamin Franklin (1748)

Close encounters: engagement and participation in the Museum and beyond

Opposite: Family learning at the Manchester Museum.

Below: Mummification of oranges at 'Unearthed Ancient Egypt' Big Saturday at the Manchester Museum.

Below right: The BBC 'Planet Dinosaur' Big Saturday at the Manchester Museum, October 2011.

The Manchester Museum has provided free admission since it first opened its doors in 1890. In the beginning, around 100 visitors attended each day. Today, the Museum runs over 250 public events and receives more than 350,000 visits each year. It is a hub of activity for people from all sorts of backgrounds and of all ages.

From babies to grandparents, the Museum receives over 150,000 family visits per year and has activities, resources and events specially designed for the whole family. 'Big Saturdays' is a hugely popular monthly drop-in event that includes performances, talks, workshops and activities. Museum staff, academics, artists and organisations share their research, expertise and knowledge on key topics linked to the collections. For example, Dinosaur Big Saturday was developed in partnership with the University's School of Earth and Atmospheric Sciences and included a Skype link with stars of the National Geographic programme *Jurassic CSI*, alongside film screenings of dinosaur animations for the under-5s, workshops and talks led by palaentologists and curators. Fast-paced, fun and full of interesting facts, Big Saturdays offer opportunities for the whole family to learn and participate. Often we will

undertake large-scale, whole-family events which relate to wider programmes, such as tie-ins to BBC television series or annual initiatives such as Black History Month, or the respective Manchester Literature, Histories and Science Festivals.

As well as working with festivals and organisations, visitors provide insight and ideas for participatory programmes. The Museum's two out-of-school Youth Boards (junior: 8–13 years and senior: 14–18 years) have been running for over a decade. The Museum also hosts a branch of the Young Archaeologists Club. In addition to advising on exhibitions and gallery displays and working closely with Museum staff, they develop and often run activities for the public and events and workshops for other young people in the city, including a bio-blitz and community dig in the local park, sustainability question time panel event and collection tours.

Adult visitors tell us how they regularly encounter the unexpected in the Museum – both in terms of the

collections they encounter and the activities and events on offer. Collection displays, exhibitions and events aim to encourage visitors to reconsider their connections to the natural world and environs, to contemporary culture and Manchester. Activities to complement this

Above: 'After Hours' event at the Manchester Museum: 'Ancient Worlds' and contemporary Arabic dancing.

> *It is a privilege to handle real objects from the Museum's collection. It is amazing… The volunteers are very passionate about this, which is brilliant.*

Museum visitor

Left: Members of the Manchester Museum branch of the Young Archaeologists Club digging on the Whitworth Park Community Archaeology Project in September 2011.

Manchester is a diverse city, and the Museum works hard to engage local communities, many of whom have rarely or never visited museums. By collaborating with communities to provide different perspectives on the world and world histories, the Museum's and visitors' understanding of the collection is enriched. Community engagement takes many forms – from long-term partnership exhibitions and targeted volunteering programmes to consultative groups, recorded interviews, and celebratory and community-led events. It aims to provide more opportunities for a wider range of people to participate in the life of their (often local) Museum.

The Manchester Museum has a long-established commitment to working with volunteers. Throughout the 20th century and into the 21st it has involved them in the care and interpretation of collections. Volunteers bring fresh enthusiasm and motivation to a variety of roles and projects, providing an outlet for new skills and perspectives and helping the Museum

Above: Sudanese musician, Awad Absin, playing in the Manchester Museum, at an 'After Hours' event.

Below right: Counting the legs of a woodlouse. Models of insects and other minibeasts are an excellent educational resource for all age groups.

approach include world music, courses of all shapes and sizes from community archaeology to wildlife photography and social 'After Hours' events in which artists, scientists, filmmakers and writers animate our collections in special one-off performances.

We are extInked!

To celebrate the opening of the 'Living Worlds' gallery in 2011, the Manchester Museum has teamed up with Manchester-based artists' collective, Ultimate Holding Company (UHC), to present 'we are extInked' – an exhibition documenting the story of the unique arts and ecology project extInked launched in 2009, in the year when the world celebrated Charles Darwin's bicentennial birthday. Artist Jai Redman created a series of 100 original drawings, each depicting one of the most endangered British species. From the diminutive Erratic Ant (*Tapinoma erraticum*) to the largest of the dolphins, the Killer Whale (*Orcinus orca*), each species was meticulously studied, reproduced and catalogued. The results of this art-ecological enquiry were published in a 230-page almanac. Furthermore, with the assistance of prominent conservation charities and the tattooists from Ink vs Steel, all illustrations of endangered species were permanently tattooed onto 100 willing volunteers, with the particular likeness of the endangered species of their choice. The result of this unique performance was a committed army of ambassadors for threatened and rare birds, fish, amphibians, reptiles, mammals, plants and fungi from around the UK. All of the 100 tattooed volunteers had a unique and life-changing encounter with contemporary art and ecology. All of them took on the role of 'ambassador' for their species, raising money and awareness for our conservation partners, and promoting education about changing ecologies and species loss. The ambassadors continue to work with the UHC artists, documenting their own journeys with their adopted species. Their contemporary activity was presented in the 'we are extInked' exhibition and in a number of events run by the Museum. The Manchester Museum and UHC continue to work together to organize additional engagement activities, such as an annual ambassador reunion.

Left: The 100 portraits of the 'extInked' ambassadors.

build links with local communities. Most of the Museum's 150 volunteers work in the galleries on handling tables, with real objects, encouraging visitors to look more closely, touch, learn and share stories.

The Manchester Museum has won widespread recognition and several awards within the employment and cultural sectors, particularly for its work to target long-term unemployed local people, by helping them re-engage with learning and improving their prospects for employment through volunteering alongside others and receiving training. This programme was, for many participants, a transformative experience, and had a major impact on their self-confidence, motivation and progress into employment. This targeted approach to volunteering – 'socially engaged volunteering'

Above: Ancient Egypt object handling with Museum volunteers.

Right: Grandparents in the Discovery Centre.

143

– is at the heart of the Museum's commitment to working with local communities and interpreting its collections in new ways.

Intergenerational learning is also central to the Museum's approach to community engagement, with programmes developed in partnership with older people and the organizations who work with them. Manchester was awarded age-friendly city status by the World Health Organization and has an active team of older people (such as 'Valuing Older People' team) working to make Manchester a great place to grow older. At the Museum and out in the community, we have a range of participatory programmes, including courses, volunteering schemes, social events and workshops, many developed by and for older people.

Beyond the Museum – in residential homes, community cafes and day centres – people encounter us through our outreach programme. Our collections travel across Manchester, introducing the Museum and its objects to new people and bringing their stories back to the Museum. The 'Manchester box', which relates to our political, social and industrial heritage, is particularly effective at unlocking stories and memories amongst some of Manchester's more socially isolated older residents. In several residential homes across the city, patients, carers and staff reminisced about their experiences at Belle Vue, which, from the middle of the 19th century, was the place to go in Manchester to have fun. Objects from the collection were accompanied by the music and songs that would have played during dance nights at Belle Vue. For older people, being able to reminisce in this way can enhance both the inner self and social skills. It involves exchanging memories with friends and relatives, with caregivers and professionals, passing on information, wisdom and skills. There are also boxes on other themes, including temporary exhibitions, and living snakes

Above: Members of the 'Forever Young' group participating in a Museum Comes to You visit at Fallowfield Library, Manchester.

"*Those Belle Vue objects bring back memories. I met my husband at Belle Vue and it was a fabulous place... Now I want to visit the Museum.*"**

Participant during 'Museum comes to You' session at day centre, Gorton and reptiles – even wheeled stuffed tigers and jaguars have gone out!

The therapeutic value of engaging with collections has also driven an off-site programme within Manchester's hospitals. One of the largest NHS sites in the region is located near the Museum, and since 2008 medical staff, patients, their families and the Schools Hospital Service have worked with staff and collections.

The role of the arts in contributing to positive mental health and wellbeing is now widely acknowledged in both museum and health sectors. Close encounters with collections offer an escape, a chance to join in, learn about the world and ourselves, to be surprised, to reflect, to care. Museums can help to restore patients' dignity and a sense of identity by providing a springboard for reminiscence and speaking about oneself, and can also help healthcare professionals develop better, closer relationships with their patients. This work, which includes NHS staff training, artists-in–residence/on-ward and Museum displays and workshops within the hospital, has been recognised by the Royal Society for Public Health for its excellence and innovation.

The Manchester Museum is about people and their place in the world. Whether within the Museum walls or beyond, it is fundamentally an organisation about engagement – with objects and collections, with ideas, with feelings, with other people, and with the past, present and future.

Right: Printmaking in the hospital.

Digital technology and the network capabilities of the World Wide Web vastly expand the possibilities for the presentation of museum collections.'

Bernard Reilly (2000)